**Popular Mechanics**

Complete Book of

# ROCKS MINERALS GEMS FOSSILS

By Donal Dinwiddie and Russell P. MacFall

Popular Mechanics Books • New York

Library of Congress Catalog Card Number 77-94062

# Contents

About the cover: This is a microphoto of a wafer-thin slice of moon rock, taken under polarized light through a microscope with a rotating stage and gypsum plates. As explained on page 114, scientists use such photos to identify minerals in rocks by the optical qualities they exhibit under such conditions. The minerals in this moon sample are plagioclase feldspar, cristobalite and ilmenite—all closely related to earth minerals with the same names.

**Popular
Mechanics**

Complete Book of

# ROCKS
# MINERALS
# GEMS
# FOSSILS

# Foreword

In recent decades interest in collecting rocks, minerals or fossils has blossomed from the hobby of relatively few individuals into the major spare-time pursuit of thousands of persons of all ages. Some specialize in rocks, others in minerals, others in crystals, ores or fossils, and still others, in lapidary work. But the single theme that binds together all these hobbyists and semiprofessionals is an interest in earth science. Too often the amateur entering this field who wants to learn about the earth and its wares is blocked by the formidable terminology and the assumed scientific background written into professional text books on mineralogy and its sister science, paleontology.

With this book, now in its enlarged and completely rewritten edition, the authors, Russell P. MacFall and Donal Dinwiddie, have successfully bridged the gap. They provide the beginner, as well as the collector who wishes to broaden his knowledge beyond his own personal experience, with a key to the door of earth science that is free of difficult professional jargon and undefined terminology. When professional terms are introduced, as they must be, it is with clear definition or example. Written in an easy style, the text makes the reader feel as if he were carrying on a personal conversation with the authors.

Both authors bring to the subject years of experience as collectors and writers. Mr. MacFall's books, *Gem Hunter's Guide* and *Fossils for Amateurs,* have become widely known and used, and Mr. Dinwiddie, as a former editor of *Popular Mechanics* and a free-lance writer on mineral and lapidary subjects, is well equipped to make the subject attractive and intelligible to a wide audience of collectors and craftsmen.

Edward J. Olsen,
Chairman, Department of Geology
Field Museum of Natural History
Chicago

# Acknowledgements

No book is ever wholly the product of those named on its title page. The authors of this book owe much to fellow collectors they have talked to and corresponded with, and the professionals and institutions which have never been too busy to advise and enlighten. Specifically mentioned should be the staff of the geology department of the Field Museum of Natural History, Chicago, and Drs. Edward J. Olsen and Eugene S. Richardson, Jr. of that department; Bevan M. French of the Office of Space Science, NASA; John Cabitto of the Gemological Institute of America; Barry Hanen of Virginia Polytechnic Institute and Keith Hartman of Lamont-Doherty Geological Observatory; Jan Hinsch of E. Leitz, Inc.; the Smithsonian Institution, Washington, D.C., Ward's Natural Science Establishment, Rochester, N.Y. and the Lizzadro Museum of Lapidary Arts, Elmhurst, Ill., and especially its chairman, Russell Kemp, for sharing their wealth of photographic materials; Mrs. Mary A. Root and Breck P. Kent for their expert photography of minerals and fossils; Mrs. Sue Pitts of Jackson, Miss., for permission to use her husband's plans for building a display case; and our wives for their patience with husbands preoccupied with earthly and earthy things.

Crystals of gem topaz in matrix form a background for a faceted topaz gemstone. Fine topaz is often yellow with a hint of orange or golden brown, but it may also be blue, pink, green, red, sherry colored or colorless. A yellow quartz, citrine, is often sold as the more valuable topaz but real topaz is heavier, more scratch-resistant, and has more sparkle.

## Chapter I

# Earth's Mysterious Bones

*"The earth with its store of wonders untold."*
—Robert Grant

It begins with one rock, then another and another, until before you know it, you have enjoyed a lifetime of rocks. You keep discovering new beauties and mysteries hidden beneath their drab surfaces. You learn of rocks that bend or float or burn or contain water; of others made of threads, needles, or opalized animal bones. You find rocks shaped like crosses, pencils, roses or chrysanthemums. You learn how to distinguish between real gold and "fool's gold", rubies and garnets, diamonds and glass, and other real and imitation gemstones. You learn where to look for ores or gems or fossils and have a good chance of finding them.

You discover rocks that can be made to glow in the dark, and others that grow as sparkling crystals according to immutable atomic laws. You learn about rocks you can taste or smell, see double through, or, as Columbus did, make into a compass. And you find that you can make stunning jewelry from stones that hide their beauty under a dull skin that is nature's varnish.

Since earliest times, the intriguing rocks have been man's companions and his gods. He treasured their beauty and utility, and their mysterious qualities fired his imagination. He hunted with stone clubs and flint-tipped arrows; he worshipped such idols as Islam's sacred stone in the Kaaba in Mecca; and he decorated himself with stone ornaments. Not being able to explain what the rocks were or where they came from, early man invented charming theories about them. To him, gemstones were created when a storm god, jealous of the rainbow's beauty, broke it so that its pieces fell to earth. Fossils—those stony casts of once-living things—grew in the earth from seeds fallen from the stars. Crystals were water turned to ice by the pressure of mountains. Some even believed that certain stones could reproduce themselves, a plausible theory to those who have noticed that crystals do grow in precisely repetitive shapes.

### The Magic Stones

Given such theories, it was natural that early man would attribute magical powers to stones. Thus a ruby protected the wearer against unhappiness, bad dreams and lightning. Sapphire made one wiser and guarded against poverty and snakebites. Turquoise insured prosperity and protected against accidents. Aquamarine guarded one in battle and, if that failed, bloodstone or topaz helped to heal one's wounds. Insomniacs needed a moonstone to help them sleep. Dowsers needed jasper to help them find water; alcoholics, an amethyst to keep them sober. Hesitant public speakers or bashful suitors could find courage by owning a sardonyx. Lovers needed a diamond to insure love and harmony and to ward off anger. Once married, they should have an emerald to insure domestic bliss; it would also help to soothe their eyes. For those who wanted to become invisible, opal was the stone of choice. This, of course, made it quite popular with thieves.

These old superstitions may seem amusing but lovers still buy diamond engagement rings, and birthstones with symbolic qualities and benefits continue to be popular. We still cherish

**1. Some minerals are made up of fibers, like this chrysotile asbestos, which is a form of serpentine. Satin spar, tigerseye and jade are other fibrous minerals.**

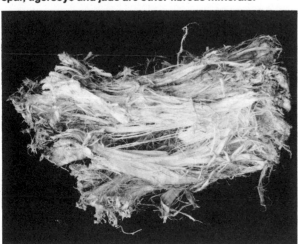

our superstitions, and we still go to the earth for our metals, our jewels, and the building stones of our civilization. We also go there to learn history, for the story of our planet and the life that has existed on it is written in the rocks. It has been a turbulent history, a tale of never-ceasing change, of fire and ice, catastrophe and quiet evolution. It is also a tale of strange beasts and plants that once flourished and now only exist as ghostly fossils of the living.

## Moon and Mars Rocks

Today we even go beyond the earth—to the moon and Mars—to collect rocks that will tell us about our universe and how it came to be. Although only a fraction of the 843 pounds of rocks collected from the moon have been analyzed to date, already we have learned much. We know that the moon is made of rocks formed by the cooling of molten magma, and they contain the same chemical elements as earth rocks formed the same way, although the amounts of the elements differ. Thus, moon and earth rocks are not identical twins but close enough cousins to have the same names.

Unlike earth rocks, however, moon rocks contain no detectable moisture, so they cannot react with water to form limestone or shale, or to "rust" as earth rocks do. As a result, moon rocks look much younger and fresher than earth rocks, even though most found so far are at least as old (and, in some instances, a billion years older) than any rocks that have been found on earth.

Still, mysteries remain. The moon has no magnetic field like the earth's yet there is mag-

netism in the old lunar rocks. Where did it come from? We can detect many moonquakes in the moon but they are like firecracker explosions compared to our massive earthquakes. What causes them? Chemically the moon is more like earth than the sun or the meteorites scientists have examined, but the moon's composition differs enough from earth's to suggest that it did not separate from earth. If not, then how was it formed?

These are mysteries we leave to the experts, for few of us will have the chance, or the special knowledge needed, to analyze rocks from other planets or satellites. And there are mysteries enough remaining in the rocks of earth to reward several lifetimes of study.

If you are like most people, the mysteries begin when you first pick up a rock whose color, shape, luster or pattern catches your eye, and you wonder what it is. Perhaps a knowledgeable friend tells you that it is a piece of sandstone, made up of tiny, worn quartz crystals, cemented

**3. Few quartz crystals are as tall as this 29-inch high, 350-pound specimen from Arkansas, but many display the characteristic six-sided, pencil-like shape. The ancient Greeks believed crystals were water turned to ice by the pressure and cold of high mountains.**

**2. Magnetite or lodestone demonstrates its attraction. The compass used by Columbus had a sliver of magnetite for its needle.**

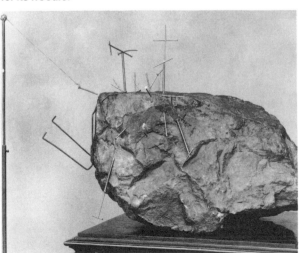

4. Staurolite's twin crystals usually intersect at 90- or 60-degree angles. When they intersect at 90 degrees they are called "fairy crosses."

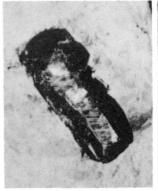 

6. Color may deceive you. The ruby crystal in limestone at left may be the same red color as the garnet crystals in mica schist at right. But different crystal structures will tell you which is which, as explained in Chapter Three.

## How the Rocks Grow

All rocks are mixtures of minerals like the quartz and feldspar in granite, and much of the earth's crust is made up of such minerals. But what is a mineral? It is a product of nature, not of man and not of life, and it is so well organized internally that it assumes a typical external shape. Thus a quartz crystal, allowed to grow free, assumes a characteristic six-sided, pencil-like shape. Other minerals form in cubes like salt, octahedrons like diamonds, or some other characteristic shape that helps you to identify them, as explained in Chapter Three.

Not all crystals have a chance to grow freely and take the shape their atomic structure decrees. When they do have the chance, they become the real flowers of the mineral kingdom. As you will learn in Chapter Four, most gemstones are found as crystals and what makes them gems is their beauty, durability and rarity.

If your interest is aroused by what you learn about the first stones you pick up, you go on to discover more fascinating facts about what you have found. Take quartz as one example. In its clear, colorless rock crystal form, it is not only made into jewelry but also into the crystal balls that soothsayers use to predict the future. And, indeed, if you look into a polished crystal ball long enough, your optic nerves may be temporarily numbed to the point where you think you see visions. But what about purple quartz? You have seen a lot of it but you know it by another name—amethyst. Indeed, many familiar gemstones—bloodstone, agate, tigerseye, citrine, carnelian, onyx, sardonyx—are basically quartz that has been colored or patterned by other minerals. So is the flint Indians used for arrowheads. And so is petrified wood, in which

together, and stained a gaudy red by iron oxides, like some sandstones in the Colorado Plateau. Or perhaps your friend tells you that it is granite, made up of the crystals of quartz and a common mineral called feldspar, all of which formed into a granular mass as the molten rock cooled.

5. The needle-like cluster is made up of crystals of a rare ore of nickel, millerite, shown here emerging from a vug (cavity) in a calcite crystal matrix.

quartz has replaced the wood fibers while retaining the living form of the original tree.

Quartz has another, perhaps more valuable, characteristic than the beauty and hardness that make it suitable for gemstones. It is piezoelectric—which means it can produce electricity when pressured by sound waves. Thin wafers of quartz, ground to precise thicknesses, transmit sound waves at fixed frequencies, making them invaluable in radio controls and other scientific applications calling for this quality.

### Gold in Brooklyn

Quartz is also frequently associated with gold, and you don't have to travel to the West to discover this, as a boy in Brooklyn demonstrated. The boy had faithfully attended lectures on earth science at the Brooklyn Children's Museum. His father, employed in a building that also housed an assay office, fueled the boy's interest by bringing home rocks discarded by the assayers. One night his contribution was a shapeless mass of milky quartz in which the boy saw promise. Excited, he took it to the museum the next day. The lecturer discouraged him but, at the boy's insistence, broke it open. To his own astonishment and the boy's delight, inside were ten good gold specimens.

Chance plays a part in such a find, but only as it is teamed with knowledge and curiosity can it become significant. In April, 1928, while pitching horseshoes with his father at their home in Petertown, West Virginia, W. P. (Punch) Jones unearthed with one toss an unusual looking pebble. "See, I have found a diamond," he said to his father. Both laughed and he put the stone in his pocket. Fifteen years later, he read a description of diamond crystals and recalled the incident. He sent the pebble to Professor R. J. Holden at the Virginia Polytechnic Institute, who authenticated it as the largest diamond ever found in the eastern United States. This "Punch diamond," as it is called, weighs 34.46 carats.

### Diamonds in the U.S.

Diamond discoveries in the United States are not as rare as one might think. Diamond finds from 18 different states have been authenticated. In the Midwest and Appalachian regions, these were usually isolated finds of single diamonds brought there by glaciers or rivers. But more than 500 diamonds have been found in California, and about 100,000 (including one weighing 40.23 carats) have been taken from the Crater of Diamonds State Park near Murfreesboro, Arkansas. You can go there and, for a fee of $2 a day, hunt for them yourself and keep any that you find.

Some mineral discoveries are out of this world. One night in 1917, an Iowa farmer named Harvey Meevers and his neighbor saw a blinding flash of light in the sky. Later, Meevers turned up a heavy object as he cultivated his cornfield near Mapleton, Iowa. He stored the 108-pound mass in his barn and showed it to a few neighbors. By coincidence an article on meteorites appeared a few weeks later in *National Geographic*. A neighbor called Meevers' attention to

7.  Diamonds, left, and quartz crystals (called Herkimer diamonds), right, may both be clear and colorless. The crystal shapes and greater hardness distinguish the real diamonds, which were found in Wisconsin and Alabama.

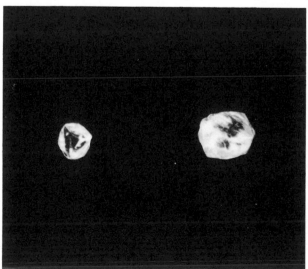

8.   You see double when you look through a piece of Iceland spar calcite, which divides a ray of light into two rays.

the article. He wrote the Field Museum of Natural History in Chicago about his discovery. Experts from the museum arrived quickly and bought the meteorite for its collection, which is one of the most important in the world.

### Gemstones from Space

Meteorites are not always just the stony or metallic mixtures of iron and nickel that make up their mass. Small diamonds have been found in meteorite fragments from a crater in Arizona, and gemologist George F. Kunz of Tiffany & Co. reported that gems were cut from yellowish green peridot stones he obtained from the meteoric iron on Glorietta Mountain, New Mexico. So there are gemstones like our own in outer space. There may be life there, too. Tests of the atmosphere on Mars and its rocks (which *do*

contain water) show the presence of most of the materials needed for the creation of life.

Fortune is as unpredictable in the hills of Maine as it was for Harvey Meevers in the fields of Iowa. One afternoon in 1820 near Paris in Maine's southwestern Oxford County, two college students, Elijah L. Hamlin and Ezekiel Holmes, stood on a hill admiring the glow of the sun setting behind the White Mountains. Suddenly Hamlin saw at his feet a quick gleam of green. It was a fine crystal of tourmaline, a gem mineral of many colors. In this way the great gem treasures of Maine first became known. From the hill, named Mt. Mica, Hamlin and his family collected hundreds of crystals that are still treasured in the museums of the world. Many more were cut into costly jewels. As a commentary on what rock collecting may or may not lead to, one of the family, Hannibal Hamlin, later became Abraham Lincoln's vice president during Lincoln's first term.

Few realize what a land of mineral plenty America is. Almost as soon as the early colonists arrived, they began prospecting for ores that could be made into tools, utensils and weapons. At Saugus, Massachusetts, just north of Boston, they discovered iron ore and built a smelting furnace. In Bergen County, New Jersey, they found a copper deposit that was worked until 1903. During the 1800s, gold was found in Georgia and North Carolina, copper in Michigan, lead near Galena, Illinois (then called Fever River), and an abundance of iron in Minnesota.

Rich silver mines found in Mexico in the mid-16th Century encouraged Spanish explorers to

9.   Crystals may form in orderly fashion, as did the iron-nickel crystals (called Widmanstatten figures) in the meteorite at left. Or they may seem to grow with abandon, like the "ram's horn" selenite crystal emerging from its matrix at right. But both are following atomic laws that predetermine the shape they will take.

tives were making exquisite castings of gold for jewelry using the *cire perdue* or lost wax process. (Your dentist probably learned the same technique for making fine inlays, which may be one reason many dentists take up jewelry making as a hobby.) Native Indians had also located useful and decorative non-metallic minerals. They made tools and weapons of obsidian, flint and jade, and used agate, azurite, turquoise and more than 80 other kinds of ornamental stones.

## A Copper Bonanza

Nor were the Indians selfish about their finds. In 1608, friendly Indians gave a piece of native copper from the Lake Superior region to Samuel Champlain, the founder of Quebec, and, by the 1840s, skilled Cornishmen who left their own depleted mines were working in the virgin copper mines of Upper Michigan's Keweenaw peninsula. At first they dug for large masses of the metal but then they discovered richer returns from pellets of copper in small cavities called vesicles in the lava. An even richer yield, according to tradition, was discovered by a convivial saloon keeper, Billy Royal, who persuaded a companion to help him hunt for some runaway pigs. In a pit dug by prehistoric miners, they found the pigs and a gleam of copper. It was in

10. Nestled in the Colorado mountains, Silverton was once a boom mining town for silver and gold. Today, rock collectors still find rhodochrosite and tungsten ores in nearby mine dumps.

move up into the American southwest in search of fabled golden cities. They found none although elsewhere, especially in Central and South America, natives had obviously discovered gold and become extremely skillful in working it. Long before the Spanish arrived, the na-

11. How Chestnut Street in Leadville, Colorado looked when the boom for mining silver and lead were at their peak. Today, the world's largest molybdenum mine is located not far from Leadville.

**12. Group of miners working on the Comstock Lode pause for a rest at Gold Hill, Nevada, about 1865.**

the form of a conglomerate rock cemented together with a rich abundance of copper. The first shaft of the fabulously successful Calumet & Hecla mines was sunk in the pit where the runaway pigs were found.

California's gold rush was set off by a carpenter, James W. Marshall, building a sawmill near present-day Coloma for Colonel John August Sutter. In a ditch dug to carry off the mill stream, Marshall early one morning in 1848 found several yellow specks of metal. Sutter and he tested them; they were gold. When the word got out, some 50,000 adventurous souls headed for the golden shores of the Pacific. Most of them were unlucky in California but, for the next decade, disappointed gold seekers found work and sometimes wealth in the mines of the Comstock lode near Reno, Nevada, one of the great silver bonanzas of the world. Others found first gold and then copper at Butte, Montana, silver at Leadville, Colorado, gold in Colorado and the Black Hills of South Dakota, and the mineral riches of Arizona and New Mexico.

The experts said that gold could never be found at Cripple Creek, Colorado, but cowboy Bob Womack, who kept his eyes on the ground as he rode, proved them wrong. His piece of gray rock bubbled with gold when it was put on top of a hot stove. Womack staked his first claim in 1890, but like many who make the initial discovery, he profited less than others who followed. A

Colorado Springs carpenter, Winfield S. Stratton, picked up mining claims in the area, developed them slowly and made them yield millions. In one room-size pocket of the Cresson mine at Cripple Creek, gold crystals worth $1,200,000 were scraped from the glittering walls.

### A Blacksmith's Aim Was Bad

A major discovery of silver in Canada is variously credited to a blacksmith and two men laying ties for a railroad. According to one story, the blacksmith threw a hammer at a fox, missed, and the hammer broke off a chip of silver-bearing rock. In the other version, the track workers sank their picks into the lode. In any event, the discovery became the great Cobalt, Ontario silver mines that later "mothered" the financial development of gold, silver, copper, cobalt and uranium in Canada.

While luck played a role in all of these finds, the amateur discoverers—whether cowboy, blacksmith, saloon keeper, or the boy who found gold in Brooklyn—all had two things in common: sharp eyes and an intense curiosity about rocks and minerals. With these qualities, you can find valuable minerals that others have passed over as worthless rocks. That is how gem-quality jade was found in the barren hills of Wyoming. Thousands of pioneers had trudged

13. How miners winnowed gold from dry stream beds when there was no water for panning, as pictured by Harper's Monthly magazine in the late 1800s. Gravel and dirt were sifted and shoveled onto a blanket which was then tossed in the air. Breezes carried away lighter dirt leaving the heavier black sand containing gold flakes. The same technique can be used today.

over these hills along the Oregon trail; hundreds of cowboys had herded cattle there, but for a century the green boulders lay unrecognized all over southwestern Wyoming.

### The Green Gold Rush

Then, in the early 1940s, so the story goes, a mild-mannered, elderly man named Corbin rode a bicycle from his home in Oregon into the Lander, Wyoming area. He had come to collect fluorescent agates in the Sweetwater river valley. Besides agates, he returned to Lander with a fist-sized green rock. After showing it to a Lander resident, Biford Foster, he remarked "This is jade, and I would rather have a mine of it than a gold mine." Next day he left on his bicycle, but the memory of his remark lingered. Out of it grew a local search for jade and, as the news got out, what became known as the green gold rush. The fever has abated by now but vacationing visitors still roam the hills prospecting, and several Wyoming mines produce a fair quality jade.

### Radioactive "Gold Dust"

While hundreds combed the Wyoming hills for jade, thousands stampeded to the even more desolate Colorado plateau in Colorado, Utah, New Mexico and Arizona. They were looking for uranium, the radioactive "gold dust" that fuels nuclear power, and some had been found in the Colorado plateau. Feverish stock trading, claim

jumping, conflicts between inhabitants and the swarming fortune hunters, even murder, ensued. A few became millionaires but many lost their hopes and some their lives in this deadly country. Such is the pattern of mining booms, and the uranium rush was one of the greatest—and perhaps the last—of such booms in America.

Not that America's storehouse of mineral treasures has been exhausted. Far from it. Patient development today is opening up new sources of lead and zinc ores in Tennessee and new copper mines in Arizona, and throughout the west the rising price of metals has justified reopening long abandoned mines. In addition, a growing number of amateurs—now well over a million in number—are finding gem minerals, ores and fossils across the face of America.

They are not fortune hunters looking for quick riches. What attracts them is the thrill of finding something beautiful, rare or mysterious. Such are the dull rocks that fluoresce in brilliant colors under ultraviolet lamps that are commonly called black lights; collectors with portable black lights still find these rocks in the big spoils piles of waste material from the zinc mines at Franklin, New Jersey, and in the other areas that are listed in Chapter Five. It was interest in the phenomena these rocks exhibit that led to the television picture tube, fluorescent lighting, detergents that make laundry whiter, dramatic stage effects, and new crime detection techniques.

14. The white coating formed by weathering helped conceal this nephrite jade from Wyoming cowboys and pioneers moving westward. But broken boulders and tips polished by wind-driven sand were visible as jade to sharp eyed searchers who knew what to look for. Jade is still being found in the Wyoming hills.

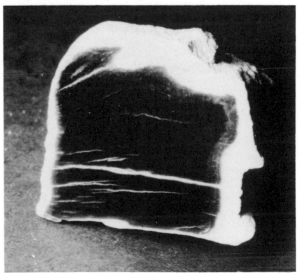

15. These trilobite fossils (Phacops rana from Sylvania, Ohio, left and Calymene celebra from Lemont, Illinois, right), are ancestors of 75 percent of the species living on the earth today, including the crabs, lobsters and insects.

16. This reconstruction of a soft-bodied animal with a spade-shaped tail, fins and a long snout with teeth was made from fossil remains found in Illinois. Called the Tully monster (Tullimonstrum gregarium) after its discoverer, Francis Tully, it still has scientists puzzled.

At Sylvania, near Toledo, Ohio, at Antelope Springs, Utah, and at several places in New York, Illinois and Wisconsin, collectors eagerly search for distant ancestors of life called trilobites. These buglike sea-bottom scavengers suddenly appeared early in evolutionary history six hundred million years ago. They evolved in a great variety of species, some fantastically ornamented, some more than two feet long, and some blind and about the size of a pinhead. Trilobites had segmented bodies with a jointed, horny armor that acted as an exterior skeleton. They are direct ancestors of about three quarters

of all existing animal species, including shrimp, lobsters, crabs, barnacles, spiders, centipedes and insects. The making of a representative collection of trilobites can become a lifelong pursuit, and they are only one of a long list of fossils of leaves, ferns, shells, fish and other forms that collectors are finding today. You will learn more about them in Chapter Six.

Amateurs are also still finding gem minerals and ores. In 1971 a boy using a metal detector discovered a chunk or "float" of copper that weighed nearly five tons on a farm near Calumet, Michigan. A year later three men un-

17. Looking like Eskimo carvings or strangely shaped fossils, these are concretions formed where sediment collected and hardened around a rock nucleus. They are pseudofossils.

covered a rich pocket of tourmaline crystals on Plumbago Mountain in Maine; one of the crystals was reported to be 13 inches long and to weigh 15 pounds.

### Prospecting in New York City

As this book was being written, one of the authors saw fine specimens of beryl (the gem family to which emerald belongs) a collector had just brought back from New England, deep red agates flecked with blue another had found recently in Mexico, some gaudily colored flint another had uncovered in Ohio, and several ounces of gold still another collector had recently extracted from a rock crevice in California. And, as soon as the book is finished, the same author plans to follow up a lead he obtained on the location of some tourmaline crystals not far from Shea Stadium in New York City. That is not as outlandish an idea as you might think, considering the fact that museum quality stones—notably garnets—have been found under the streets of Manhattan.

Most of the great collections of minerals, gems and fossils in the United States were assembled largely by enthusiastic amateurs. After spending a lifetime enjoying their treasures, they gave them to museums for others to enjoy and to learn from. Indeed, if you want to learn how to recognize minerals—and the variety of forms and colors in which they occur—a good start would be to visit museums in your area and study their carefully identified specimens.

### Some Famous Collections

An outstanding collection is maintained by the National Museum of the Smithsonian Institution in Washington, D.C. (don't overlook their magnificent black Roebling opal from Virgin Valley, Nevada; the blue Hope diamond; and the Canfield collection of zinc minerals, including fluorescents, from Franklin, New Jersey). Other notable collections are maintained by the American Museum of Natural History in New York City; the Academy of Natural Sciences and Bryn Mawr College in Philadelphia; the Field Museum of Natural History in Chicago (don't miss their jade and meteorite collections); the Lizzadro Museum in Elmhurst, Illinois; Cranbrook Institute in Detroit; the Golden Gate Park museum in San Francisco; and the collections maintained by Harvard, Yale and other leading universities.

A source of information closer to home may be one of the amateur mineral clubs or societies scattered across the nation. Some 70,000 rock and fossil collectors, and lapidaries who shape and polish gemstones, belong to these clubs. In turn, the clubs belong to regional federations and a national federation which together publish more than 1,000 bulletins annually and hold as many annual shows. Each year a list of these organizations is published in the April Rockhound Buyer's Guide issue of the Lapidary Journal, (see Appendix 4).

If you attend a mineral club meeting, you will meet people with a variety of interests in rocks. Some collect minerals, ores or crystals; others turn drab rocks into beautiful jewels; still others find in fossils fascinating clues to the earth's past and its probable tomorrows. Most will be happy to share what they know and to show you their collections, for they have found that being the curator of one's home museum is a rewarding experience.

Delight in possession and pride in craftsmanship are certainly basic incentives to those who collect and work with rocks. Perhaps even deeper, almost subconscious, is the feeling that to touch rocks and become familiar with their qualities brings one closer to understanding the fundamental bond we have with the mountains, valleys, seas and creatures of our earth.

As you learn about these bones of our earth—the rocks—in the chapters that follow, you may experience that feeling. It is an exciting one.

*Chapter II*

# Our Restless, Rocky Earth

*"Rough quarries, rocks and hills whose heads touch heaven."*
—Shakespeare

If the landscape outside your window looks serene and complete, that is an illusion. It was probably under an ocean or a glacier once, and it will be again. Its contours are being reshaped continually. Its rocks may be symbols of strength and stability but, like the earth whose crust they form, rocks and soil never stop changing. Mud and clay become shale and shale recrystallizes into slate. Plants become first peat, then lignite, and then coal. Soft sandstone becomes hard, tough quartzite and chalcedony. Granite changes to a banded rock called gneiss (pronounced "nice"). Sea creatures become limestone which in turn becomes marble. Air, water, heat, cold, pressure, wind, chemicals, bacteria and gravity then break down the rocks into separate minerals through erosion and redeposition. Having destroyed, the same forces then build by recombining the minerals into new rocks in a perpetual cycle of renewal.

18. Water and wind carved these shapes in the sedimentary clay and sandstone rocks of the Badlands in South Dakota. Many fossils of vertebrates—including ancestors of crocodiles, elephants, hippopotami and camels—were found here in the 1800s.

In much the same way, land and sea, mountain and valley have changed places repeatedly in the 4.5 billion years the earth has existed, and the changes continue today. Mountain climbers who reach a summit find rocks containing fossils that lived and died in ancient seas. Where cliffs once brooded over silent waters, grain now grows on flat midwestern prairies, and shark fossils are found in Indiana creek beds and the hills of Montana.

Making mountains and seas trade places takes time but nature has time on her side; such changes are usually gradual, even imperceptible, but nonetheless relentlessly dynamic. By themselves, though, erosion and redeposition could not maintain the diversity of elevation from mountain top to sea bottom. The earth would have been reduced to a tiresome level plain long ago if its crust had not continually raised new mountain-making masses.

A quick way to build mountains is to have volcanic eruptions of molten rocks and minerals from the hot mantle that lies just under the earth's crust. In six days in February, 1943, the Mexican volcano of Paricutin had grown to a height of 550 feet; in seven months, it had reached 1250 feet and its lava flows had destroyed the Mexican villages of Paricutin and San Juan (Figure 19). But why do volcanoes erupt where they do? And why do some mountains exist where there is no sign of volcanic activity? The answer to both questions can be found in the theory that the earth's crust is made up of segments or plates that are in constant motion.

## Floating Continents

This revolutionary geological theory began with Alfred Wegener, a German who in 1912 suggested that all the continents had once been part of a single mass which he called Pangaea. According to his theory, Pangaea broke up into two parts about 180 million years ago— Gondwanaland including Africa, Antarctica, Australia and South America, and Laurasia, made up of North America, Europe and Asia. Later the continents drifted into their present positions.

Although scientists at the time ridiculed Wegener's theory of drifting continents, there was evidence that tended to confirm it. The east coast of South America and the west coast of Africa are like two pieces of a jigsaw puzzle that would fit together were it not for the ocean separating them. The fossils of the Antarctic, Africa and South America are closely related. Fossil

mammals and birds of Canada's Ellesmere Island match those of western Europe. In addition, closely related rocks run from New England through Nova Scotia and Greenland to Scotland. Coal plant fossils from the American midwest are like those of England and Europe.

Scientists also recognized that the oceans lie in basins made up of heavy basaltic rocks, while the continents are formed of lighter rocks. In such a situation, floating continents did not sound altogether like science fiction.

The greatest merit of Wegener's theory, however, lay in the research it stimulated. Out of this came the theory of plate tectonics to explain continental drift and the forces that move continents, cause volcanic eruptions and earthquakes. These are the processes that create fresh deposits of ores and minerals.

19. The Mexican volcano Paricutin erupting in 1943. In seven months it had reached a height of 1250 feet and covered two villages with fiery cinders or lava.

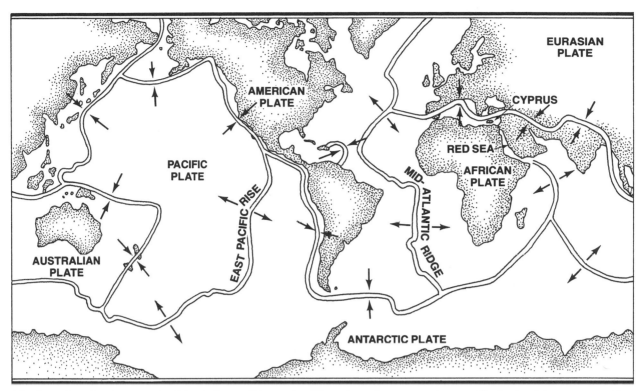

**20.** Location of major tectonic plates in the earth's crust or lithosphere. Arrows moving apart indicate plates are spreading apart or diverging, arrows moving together show plates coming together or converging.

## Moving Earth Plates

The concept of plate tectonics is that the earth's crust is made up of a mosaic of rigid plates that rub and jostle each other like ice floes in a wintry sea. Seven major and a number of smaller plates have been outlined; in most instances each plate includes both continental and ocean basin crust (Figure 20).

The American plate, for example, includes all of North America except the strip of California west of the San Andreas fault, which belongs to the Pacific plate. The American plate extends on the east to a ridge down the center of the Atlantic Ocean. This ridge is part of a chain of mid-oceanic ridges that wanders through the oceans like the seams on a baseball cover. Molten rock spurts through crevices in the ridges, forcing away the older abutting rock. As the sea floor spreads under this pressure, the continents move, too, sliding on hot, semi-plastic rock. The edges of the plates are swallowed up in trenches along the continental borders and the island chains, where the forced-down crust is melted and absorbed into the earth's hot mantle. Volcanoes are concentrated in the unstable areas where plate margins sink into ocean trenches. The Pacific plate is ringed with volcanic fire,

from the Andes north across Central America, along the Cascades into Alaska, through the Aleutian island chain, Japan and the island arc south, then west across Indonesia clear to Italy.

Where two plates rub against one another, the heavier oceanic plate usually dives under the more buoyant continental one, raising it and creating such mountain ranges as the Andes in South America, the Sierra Nevada in California, and the island arcs offshore like the Philippines and Japan (Figure 21). All these regions have had major earthquakes which can be attributed to the jostling and overriding of the great plates.

Most deep-seated earthquakes seem to occur near the ocean trenches, but shallow quakes result where the plates lock, then suddenly let go. The restlessness along the San Andreas fault and its tributary faults appears to be of such origin. Baja California and southern and central California's coastal area, part of the Pacific plate, move an estimated 2½ inches a year northwest along the San Andreas fault. If the human race lasts long enough, Los Angeles residents will look out some morning 10 million years hence and see that they are neighbors of San Francisco. Their next stop will be the Aleutian islands, which has a less temperate climate but grows its own fur coats.

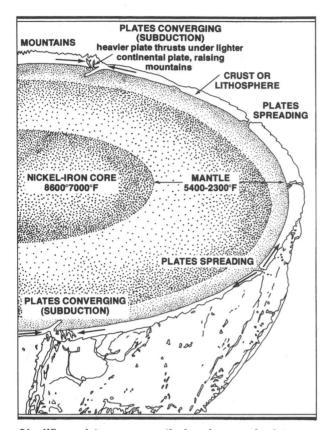

21. Where plates converge, the heavier oceanic plate may dive (subduct) under the more buoyant continental plate, pushing up such mountain ranges as the Andes and Sierra Nevada. Where plates diverge, molten magma rises through the openings, spreading them further apart. At the plate margins, sea water circulating in the emerging molten rocks as they cool and crack leaches out ores and minerals, and deposits them as rich new sediments.

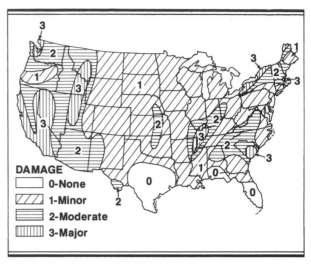

22. Your risk of experiencing an earthquake depends on where you live as this seismic risk map shows. The worst earthquake in U. S. history occurred in 1811 in southeastern Missouri, still considered a major risk area.

Africa's pressure northward toward the Eurasian plate appears to have created the Alps, just as the Himalayas may have risen where India collided with the same plate. The thrusting of the Pacific plate under the American plate is thought to have caused the Good Friday earthquake of 1964, which raised 12,000 square miles of south central Alaska an average of 7½ feet, and dropped 20,000 square miles an average of 5½ feet. That is indeed a massive rearrangement of land.

## "Hot Spots"

As the plates move, they appear to ride over "hot spots" where molten, deeply buried magma rises close to the surface. Where these "hot spots" have raised domes at the surface, mountains are created through a complicated process of rifting and filling of valleys with sed-iments eroded from the rift. If a "hot spot" stayed in one place and created volcanoes, a string of volcanoes would result as a plate moved across the "hot spot." This would explain the existence of the volcanic Hawaiian Islands and their trend northwestward as the Pacific plate moved in that direction.

Sea-floor spreading widens the North Atlantic a fraction of an inch a year, which is a measure of the rate at which it is shoving North America westward. Iceland, a "hot spot" on the mid-Atlantic ridge, is breaking apart at about 1/3 inch a year. Measurement of the age and magnetic orientation of drill cores taken from the sea floors has helped confirm these theories of sea-floor spreading and plate tectonics.

## New Ore Deposits

To anyone interested in minerals, the new geological theories hold the exciting possibility of explaining why mineral ores occur where they do. There is evidence that the seats of activity at the plate margins and mid-oceanic ridges are also the places where new ore deposits are created. Rocks formed by the molten magma that lies below the earth's crust are called igneous or fire-formed rocks and they all contain some metallic matter. As the molten rocks rise to the crust's surface at plate margins, mid-oceanic ridges and "hot spots," they cool and crack. Briny water circulating in these cracks dissolves the metallic salts in the rocks and concentrates them as sediments on the ocean floor.

23. Instead of eroding, mountains sometimes crumble, as this one did when dislodged by an earthquake near Yellowstone National Park in 1959. Forty million cubic yards of rock filled the canyon to depths of up to 400 feet. The same quake changed the park's Sapphire Pool into a geyser and exposed tracks of ancient man and buffalo around the rim of the pool.

The Red Sea basin, a site of intense crustal activity, is very rich in metallic salts, with some of the sea beds deeply layered with the mineral ores of copper, gold, silver, iron, nickel, zinc and cadmium. The Red Sea basin appears to be an earlier stage of the process that has made the island of Cyprus a source of metals since ancient times. The Romans named copper from the island; from the Latin *cuprum* or *cyprium* our name is derived. Scientists identify Cyprus as part of the bed of an ancient sea which was forced to the surface by pressure from the African plate, and brought up with it deposits like those now forming in the Red Sea.

A restudy of other areas in the light of the new theories has led some scientists to conclude that "hot spots" created by molten masses rising into the crust produced the mineral riches of Arizona, that the gold of the Homestake mine in South Dakota lies in sediments left by ancient seas, and that the new theories account for the discovery of productive zinc and copper mines near Timmons, Ontario.

Not all of nature's dramatic behavior can be attributed to the forces unleashed by plate tectonics. The most violent earthquake in U. S. history occurred in 1811 in southeastern Missouri, far from any tectonic plate margin. Three shocks splintered 150,000 acres of forest and created

Reelsfoot lake in Tennessee when the Mississippi river poured its waters into areas where the land had sunk (Figure 22). The cities of St. Louis, Cincinnati and faraway Washington, D.C. were shaken by the quakes, which were attributed to downwarping of the earth under the weight of soil washed down by the Mississippi river. Such shifting of weights and pressures on the earth's surface—a continuing process everywhere—may warp and fold the rock strata

24. Earthquakes and crustal movements may create a break known as a fault in the rock strata, as at left. Or the strata may simply bend, creating a fold that raises the strata without breaking them, as at right.

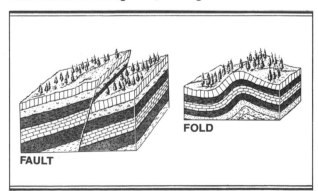

FAULT

FOLD

25. Diorama of the tip of a retreating glacier looks innocent enough compared to the mile-thick glaciers that once covered much of the midwest. They gouged out the Great Lakes' basins, formed the midwestern prairies and left behind Lake Superior agates, some diamonds, and other minerals they had brought down from the north.

below into hills and valleys without actually breaking the rocks or causing a destructive earthquake (Figure 24). Nature does its work unobtrusively at times.

### The Might of Ice

Ice takes no second place to volcanoes and quakes as a dramatic rearranger of the land and its rocks (Figure 25). Four times in the last one million years a minute drop in the world's average temperature caused snow to accumulate in the polar winters faster than it melted in the summers. The snow became mountains of ice at the Poles. With so much of earth's moisture frozen, sea levels fell, and massive mile-thick glaciers slowly oozed south over Europe and North America. Like giant bulldozers, they sheared off the rocks in their way and filled valleys with the debris they brought along.

Ice deepened the basins where the Great Lakes now rest and created the broad midwest prairies, burying beneath its spoil the roots of ancient mountains like those exposed in Canada. On their limits the glaciers formed the drainage systems of the Ohio, upper Mississippi and Missouri rivers.

Animals fled south before the slowly moving ice sheet and the mammoth grew a woolly overcoat. The last continental glaciers formed 70,000 years ago and moved as far south as northern New Jersey, southern Indiana and most of Montana. They also covered England, northern Germany and part of Russia, holding at one time nearly a third of the world's land areas in their icy grip.

The last glacier withdrew from the Midwest only about 8,000 years ago—a mere yesterday in world history. Since that time the world has grown warmer and major ice caps exist only in Greenland and the Antarctic. When the weight of ice no longer depressed the land, the land began to rise. It is still slowly rising, particularly in the Great Lakes region, a few inches a century. If this correction continues long enough, Hudson Bay will become dry land.

The ice gouged and clawed the surface with stones held in its grip, marking its course with long parallel scratches. As it retreated, the glacier left moraines—great piles of debris— along its flanks and at its tip, as well as some unusual formations. Eskers are long sinuous ridges where streams flowed in or on a glacier and dropped soil and stones. Kames are hills built by the rock deposited by a cascade. Drumlins are single hills or a series of hills formed where the glacier met with major resistance, and kettles are small lakes in depressions left where blocks of ice rested in the glacial deposits.

Northwest of Milwaukee, Wisconsin, is Kettle Moraine State Forest, a classic location for the glacial formations. Others can be seen in central New York state and Massachusetts. Bunker Hill, for example, is a drumlin. Boulders left by glaciers are often prized as lawn ornaments or as a background for bronze tablets. In isolated areas they sometimes can be seen as lone boulders balanced on bare rock surfaces. These are called erratics.

Cannonball River, which flows on the line between North and South Dakota, is named for the round stones found in its valley. They were brought down by glaciers and shaped by being rolled in the meltwater from the glaciers. They are formed of a hard sandstone, white, gray and brown, and range in diameters from one to 12 inches. Lemmon, South Dakota, celebrated a unique deposit of such stones by building a monument of them. Similar stones have been found near Rawlins, Wyoming.

The Lake Superior agates, celebrated for their patterns and color, are more widely dispersed than Lemmon's round stones, but they, too were carried from northern Canada by the ice invaders. So were some of the diamonds that have been found in midwestern states.

## Nature's Rise And Fall

Earthquakes, volcanoes and glaciers are dramatic rock formers, but the daily work of other natural forces largely shapes and distributes the rocks we find. As soon as a mountain is created by faulting, warping, folding or volcanic action, nature's leveling instincts go to work. Running water, moving ice, wind, heat and cold, chemicals, and the most powerful leveling force of all—gravity—erode the high places (Figure 26), and fill the valleys with sand, silt and gravel. Under the pressure of their own weight these sediments, often thousands of feet thick, turn into rock. Their roots are pushed down into the hot mantle beneath the crust, melt and then rise again as the material of new mountains.

As the new mountain material presses upward, it raises the rocks above it. As a result,

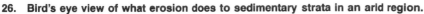

26. Bird's eye view of what erosion does to sedimentary strata in an arid region.

27. Large boulder, perhaps cracked by ice, is split apart by the force of a plant growing through it.

sandy, silty rocks and fossils are often found on top of granite peaks, relics of the water-filled valley in which they once rested.

The mechanism of degradation and weathering of the high places is as simple as it is effective. Sunshine warms the rock; the chill of night causes it to contract and crack. The bald head of Half Dome in Yosemite National Park is a striking example of the effect of such weathering on granite, which sheds thin shells where exposed to the elements.

Rain falls and seeps into crevices; the water freezes and forces the pieces of the rock apart. Plant roots, fighting for a foothold, wedge the fragments farther apart (Figure 27). A mountain stream, racing down the slope, gathers the fragments and rolls them along, using them as tools to carve its channel. At the foot of the mountain, the stream spreads its waters and drops its burden in a broad fan of sand and gravel.

The mighty Colorado river, until hobbled by dams, carried 250 million tons of the Colorado plateau downstream every year. Even as sedentary a river as the Mississippi, winding through a plain, robs the farmlands of Mid-America of enough soil annually to fill 10 million freight cars. A measure of its power and industry is the vast delta it has built from Vicksburg, Mississippi, deep into the Gulf of Mexico. The Father of Waters is also the father of several of our southern states.

A striking example of the power of running water, an example scaled to more visible dimensions, can be seen in southwestern Georgia.

Near the village of Lumpkin, south of Columbus, a miniature Grand Canyon has appeared within a mere half century. Providence Canyons started as a gully where rainwater ran off the roof of a barn. Now 3,000 acres have been carved into channels as deep as 200 feet, with spires, pinnacles and buttes mimicking those of the giant canyons of the west, and nearly as gaudy in rich gold, pink, brown, purple and black (Figure 28).

As the land's surface rises, existing streams have to fight to survive, for water is reluctant to flow uphill. Fortunately, elevation gives the streams greater power to abrade their beds. If they can cut as fast as the land rises, the regional drainage pattern survives and streams will cross a mountain range contrary to all logic of geography. The water gaps of the Appalachians are relics of such ancient stream patterns, and so are the Royal Gorge of the Arkansas River and the Grand Canyon of the Colorado river, carved in the Rocky mountain and Colorado Plateau uplifts.

28. Rain running off a barn roof started this miniature Grand Canyon near Lumpkin, Georgia. Called Providence Canyon, the area now has 3,000 acres carved up to 200-feet deep, with gaudy colored rocks and soils rivaling those in the west.

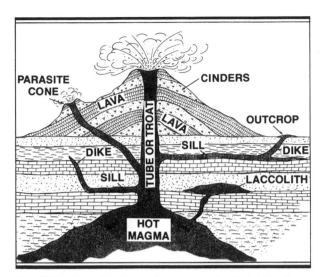

29. Volcanic action forms igneous rocks that take these typical formations. Wherever the hot rock intrudes into surrounding rock, metamorphic rocks may be formed, a process known as contact metamorphism.

high they sometimes break windows in lighthouses. A great storm in 1874 drowned the lantern of the lighthouse 100 feet above Bishop Rock, Cornwall. The California coastline with its sea stacks, caves and shattered headlands attests that the Pacific ocean belies its name.

The Great Lakes, especially savage Lake Superior, rage at times. When rich veins of silver were discovered in a tiny reef off Thunder Bay in Lake Superior, thousands of tons of stone and timber were placed in breakwaters around the reef, called Silver Islet, to protect the mining operation. Time after time winter storms tore away the barricades. When a breakwater was finally built that held the waves at bay, nature used a new weapon. The lake froze fast; fuel barges were unable to reach the mine; its pumps failed for lack of power, and the bonanza was finally abandoned. It has remained so for nearly a century.

The Lake Michigan shores near Holland, Michigan, are a perpetual reminder that wind-driven storms can tear away shorelines, tumble houses into water and destroy resort beaches. Farther south currents sweep sand around the end of the lake, and the wind whips the tawny grains into some of the world's most spectacular sand dunes.

Water driven by wind can exhibit unbridled destructive power. Storms at sea hurl huge waves against coastal cliffs, striking blows of hundreds of pounds to the square foot, tearing away the solid rock and hurling fragments so

30. Weathering and erosion carry rock fragments to low areas where they are deposited as sedimentary rocks. As the deposits build, pressure, heat and chemical actions may convert these sedimentary rocks into metamorphic rocks.

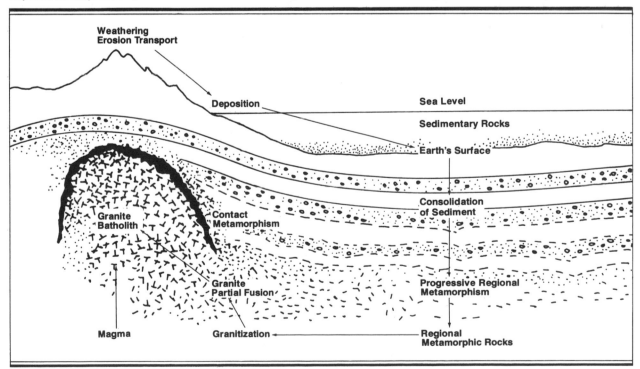

## TABLE A  COMMON VARIETIES OF ROCKS

**EXTRUSIVE IGNEOUS ROCKS**

| NAME | DESCRIPTION |
|---|---|
| Rhyolite | Fine-grained, light colored, pink or tawny. Same composition as granite. |
| Obsidian | Dark, glassy with no crystals visible to the eye. |
| Pumice | Pale gray, porous form of obsidian fragments. Will float on water. |
| Andesite | Darker than rhyolite; contains more dark minerals and little quartz. |
| Basalt | Dark, greenish gray to black lava that may acquire whitish coat in dry areas, brown coat in humid areas. Fine-grained counterpart of gabbro and most common extrusive rock. Vesicles in basalt may contain agates, amethysts, calcites, zeolites. |

**INTRUSIVE IGNEOUS ROCKS**

| | |
|---|---|
| Granite | Coarse but relatively uniform grains. Light colored with grayish quartz, white and pink feldspar, some dark hornblende and shiny mica. |
| Syenite | Like granite but less mottled with smaller, finer-grained crystals. Contains more feldspar, little or no quartz. |
| Pegmatite | Like granite but very coarse grained. May contain crystals of beryl, tourmaline, topaz and other gems, as well as rare metallic minerals. |
| Diorite | Dark colored, frequently dull gray or green. Coarse-grained like granite but contains more feldspar, less quartz. |
| Gabbro | Dark brown to black. Coarse-grained. Little or no quartz but may contain labradorite and related feldspars. |
| Peridotite | Dark, frequently greenish to black hues. Coarse-grained like gabbro. Contains olivine and pyroxene, little or no quartz and feldspar. The kimberlite in which diamonds are found is a variety of peridotite. |

**SEDIMENTARY ROCKS**

| | |
|---|---|
| Sandstone | Largely quartz grains with some feldspar, cemented together with silica, lime and iron oxides. May contain petroleum. |
| Shale | Fine-grained, compacted and hardened mud and silt derived from particles of quartz, weathered feldspar and mica and darkened by iron oxides and fossil carbons. Some types may yield petroleum. |
| Limestone | Largely calcite from precipitated calcium salts and the remains of sea life. Grain ranges from compact and crystalline to masses of visible shells (coquina) or other particles. Common colors are chalky white, gray, black but may have other color or be variegated like marble. May contain fossils and be associated with lead, zinc, sulfur and petroleum deposits. |
| Dolomite | Harder and bluer than the limestone from which it is derived. |
| Conglomerate or pudding stone | Sand and pebbles cemented together with iron oxide, silica or lime. Breccias are conglomerates in which sharp, angular fragments of stone are cemented together. |
| Chert | Form of silica found as nodules in limestone strata or stream gravels. Closely related to flint. |
| Coal | Plant tissue that has become inorganic carbon. |
| Gypsum | Calcium sulphate precipitated from sea water to form a soft sedimentary rock used in plaster and fertilizer. Crystalline gypsum is selenite, a fibrous form is satin spar, and an ornamental variety is alabaster. Anhydrite is like gypsum but contains no water. |
| Salt | Halite or rock salt is mined from deposits formed where water evaporated and they were buried under other sedimentary rocks. Forms in cubic crystals and, of course, tastes salty. |

**METAMORPHIC ROCKS**

| | |
|---|---|
| Slate | Recrystallized shale. Parts readily along flat planes to show glistening surface of fine mica particles. |
| Gneiss | Coarse grained. Looks like granite but with alternate banded stripes of light and dark mineral layers. |
| Schist | Superficially resembles gneiss but is more irregularly banded and permeated with mica. May contain crystals of garnet, staurolite and andalusite. |
| Quartzite | Quartz particles from sandstone welded together by heat and pressure to form compact, tough, fine-grained rock that comes in many colors. |
| Marble | Coarse-grained rock created when heat and pressure crystallize limestone or dolomite into calcite. |
| Skarn | Silicates formed when hot intruding rock forces its way into limestone, creating garnet, epidote, idocrase, diopside and other colorful silicate minerals. |

## How the Rocks Are Formed

As the earth is changed by crustal movements, volcanic action, or erosion and redeposition, its rocks are alternately ·squeezed, melted, cooled, abraded, dissolved and recrystallized. Understanding how these forces affect the rocks is the first step toward knowing where to look for various rocks, minerals or fossils, and how to recognize them when you see them.

When classified according to origin, rocks are divided into three major groups—igneous, sedimentary and metamorphic. Igneous—(from the Latin word *ignis* for fire) describes rocks that have risen as a molten mass from deep within the earth (Figure 29). Sedimentary rocks are formed from the concentration of sediments or particles of other rocks, minerals or organic matter. Metamorphic (from Greek words meaning change in form) rocks are igneous, sedimen-

tary or other metamorphic rocks that have been changed in structure or composition by heat, pressure or chemical action.

## Extrusive Igneous Rocks

When the melted rock, called magma, rises to the surface and is ejected, it forms the *extrusive* rocks shown in Table A. Like all igneous rocks, they are hard, heavy, and do not show banding or contain fossils (Figure 31). Although they are crystalline, the rocks have cooled so quickly that the crystals are too small to be seen without magnification. Basalt, the most common extrusive rock, forms the lava plateau that covers Washington, Oregon and parts of Idaho and Montana. The lava, which welled from huge crevices in the ground, weathers to create the soil that grows America's favorite baking potato.

**31.   Some igneous, metamorphic and sedimentary rocks**

| | | |
|---|---|---|
| **A. Granite** | **B. Rhyolite** | **C. Pegmatite** |
| **D. Obsidian** | **E. Gneiss** | **F. Sandstone** |
| **G. Schist** | **H. Breccia** | **I. Basalt** |

Rockhounds dig in the decomposed lava for rounded nodules of agate and opal, called thundereggs, that formed in gas pockets.

Basaltic lavas spread across what is now the bed of Lake Superior while other volcanic activity formed mountains of rhyolite farther south. Pebbles from the mountains and the lava flows formed a series of alternating beds of basalt and rhyolite conglomerate. Then the whole mass was tilted and permeated with metal-bearing solutions. From this region came most of America's copper for nearly a century. The fabulous gold of Cripple Creek, Colorado, was mined from the throat of an ancient volcano, and, farther south, gold and silver treasures were found where volcanic activity had raised the San Juan mountains.

Basalt is the rock that underlies the oceans. It is denser and heavier than the igneous rocks that form most of the continents. It is also the dark rock that forms the features we see as the man in the moon.

## Intrusive Igneous Rocks

Hot magma may not reach the open air but remain buried under the surface rocks. The rocks formed here are called *intrusive* rocks. They contain the same mixture of minerals as the extrusive rocks but they cool slowly enough to grow readily visible crystals. Like the extrusive rocks, they are hard and heavy with no banding or fossils. As Table A on page 30 shows, variations in color, grain texture and the amounts of different minerals each contains identify the major types of intrusive rocks.

Gold is found in quartz veins in intrusive rocks, and the ores of tin, titanium, and many of the sulphide ores of copper, nickel and cobalt are mined from these rocks or from deposits formed by the weathering and concentrations from them. The coarse-grained pegmatites are a prime source of precious gemstones (Table A).

Formations of igneous intrusive rocks come in a wide variety of shapes and sizes (Figure 29). A formation may shove up the rock of a whole region, creating a batholith (Greek for deep rock), such as the 400-mile-long faulted Sierra Nevada in California. Or it may create a laccolith, which is a baby batholith like the Black Hills in South Dakota or the Henry Mountains in Utah. Later, erosion exposes the batholith; carved by glaciers and streams, it becomes a range of mountains.

Intrusions are not always on such a grand scale. Sills are thin, horizontal sheets of rock that, while molten, have forced their way between strata of pre-existing rock. A classic example is the Palisades of the Hudson River. Dikes are long, narrow vertical intrusions. Because they are usually harder and more resistant to erosion than the rocks around them, they are easily recognized as they cut across the strata of horizontal rocks.

Nearly all igneous rocks know a delightful trick to vary their usual appearance. This variation is called porphyry, in which well-defined crystals of such minerals as the feldspars stand out against a background of a fine-grained rock (Figure 32). Some exceptional specimens are called chrysanthemum or flower rocks because the crystals display themselves like petals. Such rocks owe their origin to a sudden chilling of the magma just at the stage of forming crystals, so that the rock mass hardens around the crystals. Porphyries are known by the name of the rocks in which they appear, such as basalt porphyry.

## The Sedimentary Rocks

Igneous rocks make up more than 90 percent of the earth's crust, but nearly 75 percent of that crust is iced with sedimentary rocks. These may simply be products of the wear and tear on the earth's crust, such as the sand that forms sandstone, the silt that forms shale or the sand and pebbles that form a conglomerate rock called pudding stone (Table A). Or they may be chemical precipitates such as limestone, chemical sediments such as salt, gypsum and phosphate rock, or organic materials, such as coal.

From sedimentary beds also come petroleum and sulphur, and ores of lead, iron and zinc. These beds preserve most of our fossils, which are the dated documents of geology. As a group, sedimentary rocks are fragmentary, sandy or silty, fine grained and even earthy. They are softer and lighter than other rocks and form in stratified layers. They are usually found in lowland plains or regionally elevated plateaus. Some common varieties are listed in Table A.

Rain, wind, and the ebb and flow of inland seas across the continent sorted the fragments of older rocks and laid them down in horizontal beds, where they hardened into sedimentary rock. Water leached iron from the rocks, and iron-loving primitive bacteria extracted the iron salts from the water and concentrated them in vast sedimentary beds in Minnesota. For generations these were the main source of the nation's iron ores. Hibbing was built on a rich bed. So that it could be mined, the city was moved two miles south. As the soft ores near Hibbing played out, Minnesota turned to mountains of tough, dark red, jaspery taconite. This is ground;

magnets extract the iron; the concentrate is rolled into pellets and shipped to the steel mills.

Hibbing's relocation was not unique. A part of Bisbee, Arizona, also was moved to allow expansion of the great copper mine there. It, too, is exhausted after a century of glory. Montana's capital, Helena, was built on "pay dirt." When gold was still $16 an ounce, the dirt beneath the city was said to be rich enough to pan but not rich enough to pay for relocating the business district. If the price of gold goes much higher than it is today, Helena's city fathers may have second thoughts about relocating.

Shale, which makes up nearly half the total volume of the sedimentary rocks, is used primarily in the manufacture of cement, although some shale found in western Colorado does contain the compounds from which petroleum can be distilled.

About one-third of the sedimentary rocks are sandstone, which consists of grains of quartz with some feldspar. Some formations, such as the glass sands at Ottawa, Illinois, are almost pure, snow-white quartz. Sandstone can be soft and friable or hard enough for a building stone, such as the facings on the brownstone mansions in New York City. But the polluted air of modern cities causes sandstone to weather heavily. Its economic importance today lies in its property of acting as a porous reservoir for petroleum. It is the oil-drillers' "sand," from which they coax the stuff that keeps America moving.

Limestone and dolomite, which are cousins, are the foundations of a great quarrying industry. From southern Indiana's oolitic limestone beds comes the stone for the cold, majestic buildings that brood like cliffs over the avenues of Washington, D.C., and many other cities. Crushed limestone and dolomite provide material for road building, agricultural lime and the flux for melting iron ore. They make up about a fifth of the sedimentary rocks, and are abundant in Florida and many of the eastern and midwestern states.

Dolomite is usually harder and bluer in color than limestone, from which it is derived. Limestone beds were formed in moderately deep seas by precipitation of calcium salts from solution and an accumulation of calcareous shells, corals and other fossil materials. One of Florida's characteristic limestones is coquina, masses of tiny shells cemented together with lime.

Conglomerate or pudding stone looks just as the name suggests—a pudding of sand and pebbles held together by a cement of fine sand, lime, iron oxide or silica. One of the most unusual cements is the copper that binds together the Michigan conglomerate. Lake Superior beaches display a colorful conglomerate jeweled with red jasper pebbles in quartz. A conglomerate bed underlies the coal beds of Pennsylvania and adjacent states. Conglomerates in which the stones are angular fragments are called breccia, from the Italian word for broken.

Chert is a form of silica found as nodules in limestone strata. It weathers from them and because of its resistance to abrasion accumulates in stream gravels. Chert and flint are closely related, and both were used by Indians to make their spear and arrow points.

The American continent was invaded many times by seas. As they retreated, they left behind

**32.** When well-defined crystals of igneous rock minerals stand out against a background of fine-grained rock, they are called porphyry, as in these examples of pyroxene porphyry (left) and "flower rock" (right).

landlocked bays where the brines of the sea water would evaporate, forming beds of salt and other minerals. As this was repeated over millions of years, deep beds were built up, then buried under other sedimentary rocks. Commercial deposits of salt are mined in western New York, Michigan, Iowa, Kansas and Ontario.

Besides salt, gypsum, which is a hydrous calcium sulphate, is mined at such places as Grand Rapids, Michigan, for use in plaster and fertilizer. Minor amounts of salts of potassium and other metals are found with salt and gypsum.

Coal was formed from leaves, trees and plants that accumulated in swamps and were covered with clay. Compressed by the weight above it, the vegetable matter over some 300 million years became almost pure carbon. Peat is compacted organic matter, and lignite is peat that is on the way to becoming coal. It is often called brown coal. Both peat and lignite are fuels.

### The Metamorphic Rocks

Heat, pressure and chemically active gases and solutions will not let the rocks alone. They create the third major rock class, the metamorphic rocks. Metamorphism may bring new elements to a rock mass, or rearrange the existing elements into new minerals. Or it may change the existing rock's physical structure. Metamorphic rocks are hard and crystalline, but many of them, such as slate and schist, split easily. Many show banding of light and dark minerals. Mica is prominent in many, even showing as minute crystals in slate. Metamorphic rocks are usually found in regions that have been disturbed by crustal movements. Table A lists some common varieties of these rocks.

When a hot intruding rock forces its way into a bed of limestone, it transforms the limestone into a rock called skarn, which is made up of such interesting minerals as garnet, epidote, idocrase and diopside—all silicates gay in green and red. Pressure and heat working in a much simpler way weld together the quartz grains of sandstone into tough quartzite. Metamorphism of this type is called contact metamorphism. It occurs in relatively small areas.

Major changes can also take place throughout a whole region, turning granite into gneiss and shale into slate or schist. There are many types of schist—among them hornblende schist, dark in color; talc schist, greenish and greasy to the touch, and chlorite schist, which is lustrous and dark green. Garnets and staurolites often are found in schists.

Fine-grained dark rocks usually are the most difficult to identify because they have so few distinctive features. Is it basalt, jade, carbonaceous limestone or slate? Is it a native rock or one that hitched a ride down a glacier or in a stream? Fortunately, there are ways to tell, as we shall see in the chapters that follow. All rocks are mixtures of minerals, and minerals are made up primarily of eight common elements that combine in varying proportions to produce specific minerals. What these combinations are, and how you can identify minerals by observation and simple physical and chemical tests, is the subject of the next chapter.

*Chapter III*

# Exploring the World of Minerals

*"Let rocks their silence break."*
　　　—Samuel F. Smith

Pliny the Elder, Roman natural historian and naval leader, lost his life in the great eruption of Vesuvius that destroyed the cities of Pompeii and Herculaneum. The curiosity that drew him so close to the volcano that its fumes suffocated him shows what an intense interest ancient people took in things of the earth.

Although Pliny's work, *The Natural History,* has been called a great storehouse of knowledge, it is of interest today primarily for the minerals he mentions and the beliefs held about them. Gypsum, pyrite, azurite, realgar, quartz, lapis lazuli, and jasper were known to Pliny. So were emerald, ruby, sapphire, diamond, and the metals that had been mined for centuries before Pliny's time. He also mentions minerals that remain unidentifiable, such as amianthus, which was reputed to resist a sorcerer's charms.

Pliny was skeptical about some magical powers attributed to stones, but he reported them, and he even seemed to believe that certain stones had sexual relations and reproduced themselves.

Writers of later Roman times and the Middle Ages added to Pliny's fancies some of their own. In 1100 A.D., Marbod, bishop of Rennes, France, attributed an unusual virtue to the lodestone, magnetite. Touch a wife with it, he affirmed; if she has been unfaithful she will fall out of bed. The saintly Hildegard, a contemporary of Bishop Marbod, prescribed dropping agates in water drunk by a sick person or used to cook his food.

Bartholomew of England, in a 13th century treatise on minerals and metals, mentions asbestos and pyrite, and recommends application of an agate to strengthen sight, slake thirst and promote marital fidelity, which seems to have been something of a problem in those days. Bartholomew also advises a coral necklace for the obese to help them lose weight.

Hematite, which leaves a red streak when scratched across unglazed tile, and the Bologna stone barite, which phosphoresces when heated, fascinated medieval writers. The greatest of these was Albertus Magnus, who lived from about 1200 to 1280 A.D. In his *De Rebus Metal-*

*licus et Mineralibus,* Albertus compiled beliefs about stones from classic and Arabian sources and added some of his own, such as a stone that makes its owner invisible; others later identified this as opal. Mineralogy in Magnus' time also included such mysterious objects as the bezoar stone, and the philosopher's stone which was endowed with myriad powers. Metals were identified with our planetary system—lead with

**33. Georgius Agricola started identifying minerals by their hardness, luster and color in 1546, a practice still followed by rock collectors today.**

35

Saturn, tin with Venus, copper with Jupiter, iron with Mercury, an alloy with Mars, silver with the moon, and gold with the sun.

Because they were rare and easily identified, gems were recommended frequently as powerful amulets possessing almost any virtue that the imagination could see in them. (A few of these qualities are listed in Chapter One; others are noted in Chapter Four.)

## Beginnings of Mineralogy

While the alchemists and philosophers were formulating theories about stones, practical-minded miners and metal fabricators went quietly about their work. Use of metals goes back to at least 6000 B.C., and gave names to the Bronze and Iron Ages. Gold, copper and meteoric iron are among metals found in the native state that early man used before he mastered the art of smelting. But not until 1546 did a practical book on mineralogy appear. *De Natura Fossilium,* by Georgius Agricola, the Latinized name of a German, George Bauer, describes a number of minerals by their color, hardness and luster, qualities still used by collectors to identify minerals today. (He used the Latin word fossilium to mean things of the earth, not in the modern sense of fossils.) Agricola's *De Re Metallica* (1556) is a classic work on medieval mining and metallurgy, a distinction it shares with *De La Pirotechnia,* by Vannoccio Biringuccio, an Italian. This work, the first printed book on smelting and metallurgy, appeared in 1540. Both books are freely illustrated with charming woodcuts of miners and metal workers.

The naming of minerals was a somewhat haphazard process in the early days. Some were named for qualities associated with them; others for regions where they were found; and still others for those who had first discovered or described them.

Pyrite comes from the Greek word pyr for fire, alluding to the sparks the mineral gives off from friction. Psilomelane comes from the words for bald and black, alluding to its color and appearance; hematite, from the word for blood because of the red streak it leaves on tile. Graphite comes from the Greek word graphien, to write, and you can write with it. Pyrolusite is from the words for fire and wash, because it is added to melted glass to clear it of brown and green tints. Sphalerite, a zinc sulphide, is from the Greek word for deceitful, because it is found with lead ores but contains no lead. Medieval miners called sphalerite blende, a German word for deceiving, and miners still use that word for it.

From the Latin have come the names for orpiment, a contraction of auripigmentum meaning golden paint, in reference to its bright yellow hue; albite feldspar from albus, white; and fluorite from fluere, to flow, because it is used to make the slag in an iron furnace more liquid. From Latin also come the words for mineral (miniaria, a mercury mine) and gem (gemma, a bud). Realgar is from the Arabic rahl al ghar, which means powder of the mine, and azurite and lapis lazuli derive from the Persian for heaven because both are blue. Grossularite, a garnet that includes green among its several colors, is appropriately named for the French word for gooseberry.

Many minerals are named for the places where they were found, such as aragonite and andalusite, from the Spanish provinces Aragona and Andalusia, and anglesite from Anglesey, an island in the Irish Sea. Magnetite got its name from both a place and a legend. Pliny repeats the story that in Magnesia, a region on the border of Macedonia, a shepherd wearing iron-nailed shoes was held fast to the ground by the magnetic power of the mineral, which is also known as lodestone (Figure 2, page 12). From the same source comes our word for magnetism.

More recently, minerals were named for mineralogists and collectors. Bornite, a copper-iron sulphide, is named for the Austrian mineralogist, Ignatius von Born; prehnite, for Colonel Prehn, who first brought it from South Africa; and proustite, a silver mineral, for the French chemist J. L. Proust.

## Classification of Minerals

Until the atomic nature of matter was discovered, identification and classification of minerals lacked a sound basis. Alchemy with its efforts to transmute elements may have been the forerunner of the chemistry on which modern mineralogy rests, but the miner and collector provided more material support. By the 18th century, however, enough minerals were known and enough theory was being developed about the nature of matter to take classification beyond Agricola's practical descriptive system.

The most commonly used mineral classification is one named for James D. Dana of Yale University. It groups minerals according to chemical relationships. This recognizes the fact that minerals are—with the exception of atmospheric gases—the source of all chemical elements. Dana's groups include native elements, sulphides, chlorides, oxides, carbonates, silicates, phosphates and sulphates, as well as a number of rarer ones, such as the bromides and molybdates.

The language used for such a classification is based on an alphabet whose symbols represent the chemical elements. The chemical symbols are the "letters." Since native elements are not chemical compounds, "letter" designations such as Au for gold, Ag for silver, Cu for copper and Pt for platinum identify them. But most minerals are combinations of chemicals, such as Si for silicon and O for oxygen, the two elements that form silica or quartz. Put them together, $SiO_2$, for two atoms of oxygen joined with one of silicon and you have the "word" or formula for silica, one of the commonest of the rock-forming minerals.

But we also speak in groups of words called sentences, and a rock is like a sentence in that it is composed of a group of minerals. Granite is a "sentence", then, of such "words" (minerals) as $SiO_2$, silica, and $KAlSi_3O_8$, orthoclase feldspar, which includes the added symbols K for potassium and Al for aluminum. Granite also contains some other minerals, such as mica, but they are longer, harder "words".

Since 98½ percent of the rocks and minerals in the earth's crust are made up of only eight chemical elements, learning the language of the rocks is not quite as complex as it sounds. These elements are: oxygen (O), silicon (Si), aluminum (Al), iron (Fe), calcium (Ca), sodium (Na), potassium (K), and magnesium (Mg). The oxides, which are compounds of oxygen and one or more metallic elements such as aluminum, together with the silicates form 83 percent of the crystalline rocks. Most rock-forming minerals, such as quartz, feldspars, micas and the dark hornblendes and augite, are oxides or silicates of the eight common elements.

Fortunately, you don't have to memorize the chemical language in order to begin making field identifications of various minerals. But a knowledge of the chemical nature of minerals is needed if you intend to delve deeply into mineralogy. For a start, refer to the table of the commoner chemical elements and the accompanying discussion in Appendix 1. Then study some of the excellent source books listed in Appendix 4. You will find that most of them group minerals along the lines of the Dana system. This is a grouping that is widely followed by most experienced mineral collectors.

## Identifying Minerals

With some 2500 different minerals known, the job of identifying them sounds formidable. For-

tunately, only about 85 minerals are common enough, or of sufficient interest to collectors, to justify the search for them. And only a few dozen are of particular interest to the lapidary who works with gemstones.

Despite their chemical complexity, it is remarkable how many minerals can be identified by touching, scratching, chipping, hefting or rubbing them, or simply by inspecting them carefully. As examples, talc and graphite feel greasy to the touch and graphite will stain the fingers. You can distinguish between quartz and a glass imitation of it by touching both; the quartz will feel colder. Sometimes tasting or smelling will suffice. Halite and sylvite—the chlorides of sodium and potassium—taste salty. Sulphur and some pyrites, barites and limestones containing sulphur may smell like rotten eggs when the mineral is broken. Broken arsenopyrite may give off a garlic-like odor. Wet shale smells earthy.

But it usually takes a number of clues to pinpoint a mineral's identity, since minerals can assume many disguises. If judged on color alone, quartz can look like topaz, fluorite like amethyst, and garnets like emeralds or rubies, to cite a few examples. So the persistent mineral detective—and that is what you will become if you take up collecting—seeks a series of clues that, taken together, identify the mineral.

## Scratch Resistance

One important clue is the mineral's hardness as determined by its resistance to being scratched (Figure 34). This is measured by the

34. A small scratch made by a piece of feldspar on the bottom of this "jade" Buddha shows that it is a serpentine which is softer than either feldspar or jade.

Mohs scale, devised by a German mineralogist, Friedrich Mohs. The scale is arranged in order of increasing hardness so that each mineral will scratch those below it on the scale. It follows:

1. Talc
2. Gypsum
3. Calcite
4. Fluorite
5. Apatite
6. Orthoclase feldspar
7. Quartz
8. Topaz
9. Corundum
10. Diamond

Hardness pencils tipped with the minerals can be purchased, or a set can be made up of crystal fragments with sharp edges. Testing is done by drawing the test piece across the specimen, preferably a fresh, unweathered crystal, then wiping away any powder and examining the specimen to see whether it has been scratched, or whether it has abraded the test piece. There are several short cuts to determining hardness. Minerals about as hard as talc feel greasy; a fingernail will scratch gypsum; a copper coin is about as hard as calcite; a steel knife blade will barely scratch feldspar, and minerals of hardness 6 or above will scratch glass.

The Mexican "jade" many tourists buy is calcite dyed green after it has been carved. A pen knife will easily scratch the calcite but not real jade. During World War II, American soldiers stationed in India bought bargain "rubies" that were probably faceted from the tail lights of their Jeeps. A quartz pencil would have saved them money, since it will scratch glass but not

35. **This specific gravity balance consists of a beam arbitrarily marked off (a yardstick will do), and pivoted in a forked upright. Weight fastened on short end balances the beam, from which hang two small pans, one immersed in water. Specimen is weighed in upper pan in air and the beam is balanced by moving a small straddling weight. Marking of air weight is recorded and specimen is then weighed in lower pan in water. Specific gravity is specimen's weight in air divided by the difference between its weight in air and in water.**

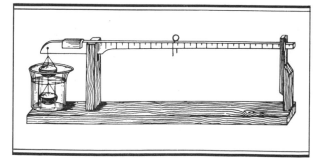

rubies. Yellow quartz (citrine) is often sold as topaz in the jewelry trade. A topaz pencil will easily scratch the quartz "topaz."

**Weight of the Mineral**

Specific gravity compares the weight of a mineral with the weight of an equal volume of water. In the field this can often be estimated roughly by hefting a specimen. Such a test is sensitive enough to distinguish barite from lighter-weight, light-colored minerals. The average weight of minerals is about 2.7 times the weight of water, so such a mineral as quartz (sp.g. 2.65) seems about normal; graphite at 2.3 seems light, and pyrite at 5.02, and lead at 7.4 to 7.6, are notably heavy. Even heavier are silver at sp.g. 10.5 and gold at 15.6 to 19.3, though unfortunately they are rarely found by collectors in heftable chunks.

Specific gravity is determined by weighing the specimen in air, then weighing it suspended in water, and dividing the weight in air by the loss of weight in water:

$$\text{Sp.g.} = \frac{\text{W in air}}{\text{W in air} - \text{W in water}}$$

For example, if the specimen weighs 4 ounces in air and 2 in water, the loss of weight is 2, which divided into 4 gives a specific gravity of 2.

The amateur can rig up a simple beam balance, as in Figure 35, to make specific gravity tests. Or they can be made with heavy liquids, such as bromoform, which has a sp.g. of 2.89. Topaz (sp.g. 3.5) sinks in bromoform, showing that its specific gravity is greater than 2.89, while quartz (sp.g. 2.65) floats. Citrine quartz is often mistaken for topaz and sold as the more costly stone, so such a simple test is useful. Sets of heavy liquids for determining specific gravity of minerals are available from supply houses specializing in earth science materials. The specific gravities of various minerals and gems are given in Table B (pages 47-55), along with a number of the other characteristics that will help identify them.

**Cleavage**

Some minerals have a property known as cleavage; some do not. Cleavage is a parting along a plane of weak molecular bonding in the structure of the mineral. It is like splitting in wood, a place where the fibers part readily. Mica, which cleaves into thin sheets, is a familiar example of perfect cleavage in a single direction.

Cleavage is described in three ways: 1. According to the direction in which the cleavage takes place. Diamond and fluorite, for example, have octahedral cleavage because its direction is parallel to the octahedral faces; topaz and mica cleave parallel to the base or flat bottom of the crystal and are said to have basal cleavage; galena cleaves parallel to the cubic faces and has cubic cleavage; calcite cleaves into rhombohedrons and has rhombohedral cleavage, and the amphiboles, such as hornblende, cleave into two directions (56 degrees and 124 degrees), and are said to have prismatic cleavage. 2. Cleavage is described as perfect, distinct, or indistinct according to the ease with which it occurs. 3. Cleavage is also described by the appearance of the cleaved surfaces, such as the pearly cleavage of feldspar and the shiny metallic cleavage of galena. The property is well demonstrated in a broken piece of granite, in which feldspar's softly glistening cleavage contrasts with the glassy fracture surfaces of the quartz grains.

### Fracture

Such minerals as quartz do not cleave. Instead, they fracture to a surface that provides a clue to their identification. Quartz, obsidian and most of the other glassy minerals, break in a shell-like (conchoidal) pattern, so called from the cupped, concave surface that results. Tough, fibrous minerals, such as nephrite jade, fracture to a jagged, hackly surface.

### Tenacity

Several other distinguishing qualities are inherent in the internal structure of minerals. Tenacity, which is the degree of resistance to breaking, is one. A tap of a hammer will crush brittle pyrite, which is often mistaken for gold, while it will merely flatten the precious and very malleable gold. An allied quality is elasticity, the ability to spring back when bent. Mica has this quality; a gypsum crystal bends readily but stays bent.

### Color and Light Clues

We recognize objects partly by their shape, but also by what light does to their appearance. Color is one of the most obvious qualities of a mineral, for example, even though it is also one of the most unreliable means of identification. White light is made up of all the colors of the spectrum. When it falls on a specimen, some colors are absorbed; those not absorbed remain to

36. The same mineral may have different shapes and surface appearances. Drawing it across an unglazed tile may leave a colored streak that helps identify it.

cause the color that we see. In some minerals color is invariable, such as the blue of azurite. Many others, such as quartz with its many colors, and tourmaline with even more, come in many hues. Jade, which we associate with green, can be blue, yellow, orange, lavender, white, black or red. The color sections beginning on pages 73, 97, and 113 show minerals in both typical and less common colors.

### Telltale Streaks

If a specimen is drawn across an unglazed tile (Figure 36), it may leave a streak of powder whose color is usually a more reliable clue than the color of the mineral itself. Hematite is a familiar example. It may look dark red or black, but its streak is always a distinctive blood red. Cinnabar, which may sometimes be mistaken for hematite, makes a lighter scarlet streak. Graphite's streak is black while molybdenite, which resembles graphite, leaves a bluish black streak. Manganite and pyrolusite, both manganese minerals, may look alike but manganite's streak is brownish, pyrolusite's is black. One way to tell gold from pyrite "fool's gold" is by the streak; gold's is yellow, pyrite's is greenish black.

Streak tests are useful for colored opaque minerals, but are of no value for most silicates, which are too hard to leave a streak or, at best, leave a white one.

Whether a crystal is transparent, translucent or opaque usually speaks more to its quality than to its identity. But in some minerals this is the determining quality. Agate, for example, is translucent chalcedony; a patterned chalcedony that is opaque is jasper.

## Luster

Luster is the appearance of a surface in reflected light. Metallic luster, which is like the surface of shiny metal, is characteristic of the metals and metallic sulphides—gold, copper, galena, pyrite. Most minerals display what is called vitreous or glassy luster, like the surface of a piece of broken glass. One reason diamond is precious is that it possesses adamantine luster, the most brilliant of all.

The character of resinous and greasy lusters is obvious from the names. So is the pearly luster often shown on a cleaved surface of feldspar and the silky luster of such fibrous materials as satin spar, a form of gypsum, and the zeolites. Some minerals appear dull and earthy, showing a lusterless luster.

A transparent piece of calcite placed over a few words of print will display another mineral reaction to light—double refraction (Figure 8 page 15). Calcite has the ability to split the light rays entering the crystal and return them as a split image. Tarnish is another useful characteristic, such as the black tarnish on native silver, the dull red tarnish on copper, the dull gray of galena, and the iridescence of some marcasites and bornite (page 102).

Some other reactions to light, such as opalescence, asterism and chatoyancy, relate primarily to gemstone minerals. They will be discussed in detail in Chapter Four.

## Fluorescence

A number of minerals, when exposed to ultraviolet light, respond with colors unlike their normal colors. This is highly diagnostic for many specimens from the zinc mines of Franklin, N.J., where the willemite fluoresces green and the calcite red (page 113). Many fluorites, such as those from England, and several uranium minerals are highly fluorescent. Chapter Five lists other minerals that fluoresce in characteristic colors, and some locations where they may be found.

## The Symmetry of Crystals

One way to identify a mineral by sight is to study the shape of its crystals, also called its crystal morphology. Micromounters, who collect crystals so small that they can be seen only through a microscope, must rely on crystal shapes for mineral identification.

The growth of crystals demonstrates how orderly nature can be. Atoms join with atoms of other elements in patterns that satisfy the play of electrical forces, creating crystal shapes that are characteristic of that blend of atoms. These crystals then grow by replicating themselves for as long as the blend of atoms that started them can supply additional material for growth.

Some sixteen million million million atoms can arrange themselves on one crystal face during an hour of its growth, according to the British Museum. In such a rush, there may be some mistakes that distort the growth and disguise the nature of the crystal. But the angles at which the crystal faces meet will always remain constant. This amazing fidelity to crystal laws can be shown by shaking some salt on a microscope slide and looking at the greatly magnified grains. They will be cubes, like a child's alphabet blocks. A few may be distorted or abraded from rubbing against each other, but where two measurable faces meet they will meet at a right

37. The edges of salt crystals forming into cubes grow faster than the center, leaving uncompleted centers when the growth is stopped.

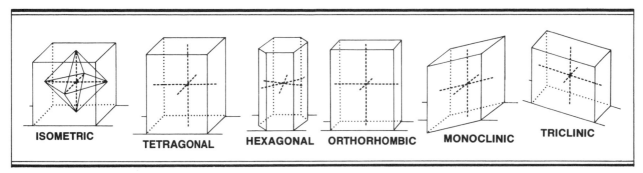

**38.** The six crystal systems are differentiated by the angle at which the crystal faces meet, and the length of the imaginary axes (dashed lines) and the angles at which the axes meet. Note that a cubic crystal, when cleaved, can become diamond shaped without altering the relationship of its axis lines or the angles at which the faces meet. So surface appearance may change while axes and interfacial angles remain the same.

angle of 90 degrees. Table salt, mined, dissolved and recrystallized under controlled conditions, remains true to the cubic crystal shape that its atomic components decreed. In nature, many cubes that did not complete their growth may show cavernous sides because the edges grow faster than the faces (Figure 37).

### The Crystal Systems

All crystals can be grouped into six systems (Figure 38). Salt belongs to the most regular one, the cubic or isometric system in which the faces meet at right angles, and imaginary lines through the center of the faces, called axes, meet at right angles and are equal in length. Other common minerals that crystallize in this system are gold, silver and copper, the diamond, pyrite, fluorite and the garnets. Besides the cube, the common forms in this system are the octahedron and the dodecahedron. The metals and diamond

favor the octahedron; fluorite the cube, and garnets the dodecahedron.

The tetragonal system resembles the isometric one except that its forms appear to be stretched-out cubes and octahedrons. While it is like the isometric system in angles, one of the axes is longer than the other two, which are of

**40.** Measuring the angle at which two adjoining faces of an hexagonal crystal of corundum meet, using a homemade shop protractor or goniometer made by fastening a pivoting protractor to a scrap plastic strip.

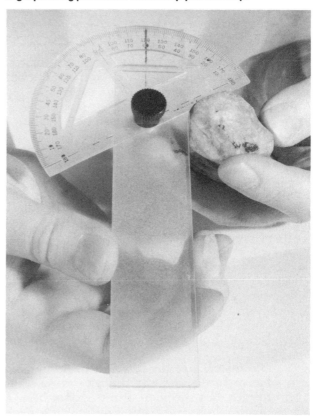

**39.** A small sampling of the many faces calcite can wear. In terms of crystal structure, it is one of the most deceptive of all minerals.

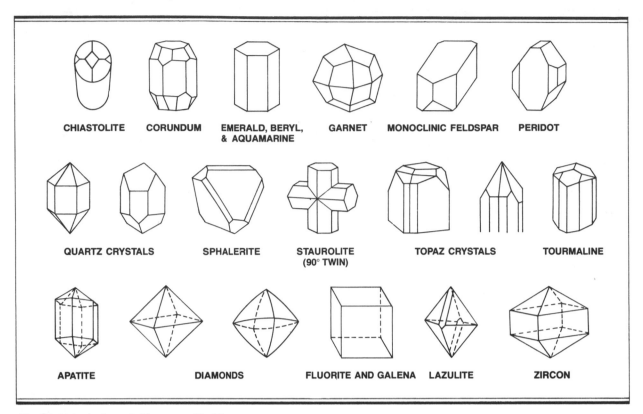

**41. Some typical crystal forms and habits.**

equal length. Zircon and rutile are representatives of this system.

A number of common minerals, such as calcite and quartz, belong in the hexagonal system. The six-sided form of quartz with its pencil-like termination of six triangular faces is familiar (Figure 3, page 12). Calcite occasionally takes a similar form but it is one of the most deceptive of minerals with several hundred crystal habits (Figure 39). Still, all are recognizable by angle measurements as being within the hexagonal system. Emerald and the corundums, ruby and sapphire also belong here (Figure 41). Many members of the hexagonal system are long and slim; others are stubby.

A typical member of the orthorhombic system might be described as domino-shaped. The faces in this system meet at right angles but no two of the axes are of equal length. As a result, length, breadth and thickness are all unequal. Barite is one of the most familiar members, with its typically tabular habit. Sulphur and topaz also belong here.

The isometric, tetragonal and orthorhombic systems are alike in that their faces meet at right angles, but the monoclinic system breaks away from this. Here the domino has been shoved out of square at two of the facing ends. The crystal leans because one axis does not meet the other two at right angles. Gypsum and orthoclase feldspar find their home here.

The triclinic system, last of the six, is a maverick that ignores all the conventions set by the other systems. Not only are the lengths of all its axes unequal, but the faces are inclined. If the monoclinic leans, the triclinic staggers. A number of beautiful minerals belong here, such as rhodonite and albite feldspar.

## Habit Among Minerals

Like people, minerals not only belong to certain basic groups, but they also develop habits that are distinctive (Figure 41). Fluorite is usually found in cubes; beryl as hexagonal prisms with flat terminal faces. Terminations of corundum crystals often give them a barrel-like shape. Tourmaline may assume a bulge-sided triangular shape. Although barite is usually flat and distinctively tabular, its "rose" habit is also characteristic (Figure 42).

Aggregates, which are masses of crystals grown together, are common among many minerals. Hematite not only forms rosettes like bar-

42. The barite rose, left, and black obsidian nodule, right, are both enshrined in Indian legends. Indians believed that dead warriors returned at night from the Spirit World, carved the roses and departed before dawn, leaving the roses widely scattered so no one would know where they had congregated. The black nodules were called Apache's tears, and they memorialized the heroic deaths of tribesmen who jumped from a cliff rather than be captured by warriors of another tribe.

ite, but it also creates aggregates of reniform (kidney-like) and botryoidal (grape-like) shapes, as do several other minerals (Figure 43). Malachite often occurs in large mammilary (breast-like), groups of compactly-rounded crystals.

Marcasite is often recognizable for its habit of serrated crystals like a coxcomb (Figure 44), native copper by its branching sprays (Figure 45), to which the term arborescent is applied, and manganese oxides by the fern-like (dendritic) patterns they write on the rocks (Figure 46).

Mica, of course, is the classic example of a foliated habit of thin sheets, like the pages of a book (Figure 47) and many of the zeolites as well as stibnite, wavellite and other minerals display

44. This coxcomb habit is a familiar form of marcasite; another is round like a gold dollar. Marcasite sometimes has an iridescent coating.

43. Botryoidal or grape-like habit in Mexican cassiterite (left), agate from Utah (center), and chalcedony geode (right) from Tampa Bay, Florida.

43

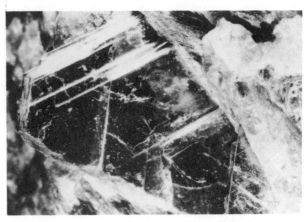

47. Micas, like this muscovite, form in foliated sheets like the pages of a book. Mica has perfect cleavage.

45. Some branching or arborescent sprays of copper are spectacular enough to frame. Others (page 120) make attractive table decorations.

aggregates of acicular (needlelike) crystals (Figure 48). These grade into such fibrous habits as asbestos (Figure 1, page 11), the hairlike millerite and the netlike (reticulated) rutile.

## Crystal Twins

Twinning is almost a habit with some minerals but rare in others, just as it is in human families. A twin is two crystals that share a face or are intergrown so that parts of the twin are in reverse position with relation to each other.

Thorough understanding of twinning demands knowledge of the complex laws of their formation, but the phenomenon is easily observed in examples of minerals that commonly occur twinned. Fluorite often forms penetration twins with the corners of one cube protruding through the faces of the other. Pyrite sometimes twins to a ball-like form in which one face resembles a cross, giving it the name iron cross twin. Quartz has a complicated structure that causes it to exist as left or right handed crystals identifiable by the presence of small faces near the termination. In a twin both sets of faces are present. Quartz is also celebrated for its Japan twins, flattened pairs joined at an angle on a prism face.

46. These fern-like (dendritic) patterns appearing in rocks are manganese oxides. They are what make the familiar moss and scenic agates so attractive.

48. Radiating, needle-like (acicular) crystals of wavellite are not uncommon. Pyrolusite, pyrophyllite, clinozoisite and such zeolites as natrolite occur in this form.

49. Staurolites form in 90-degree twins or in 60-degree twins like these.

The fairy crosses of staurolite, two crystals twinned at right angles (page 13), are highly prized and often worn as jewelry, but 60-degree twins are also common (Figure 49). A number of minerals, including chrysoberyl, cerussite, spinel and rutile, form repeated twins in which the individual crystals unite in a circular pattern (Figure 50, left). Twinning often disguises the true crystal system of a mineral, notably in aragonite which twins six individuals into a hexagonal prism, although the mineral is not hexagonal but orthorhombic.

The feldspars, orthoclase and albite, provide the student of crystallography with classic examples of twinning, such as the Baveno, Carlsbad and Manebach twins (Figure 50). The multiple twinning of thin, platelike crystals of orthoclase and albite also produces interesting optical effects. and the green-white striping of some amazonite.

## Crystal Substitutions

Minerals also know something about role playing. One mineral can replace another by chemical action without altering the form of the replaced mineral. The new mineral assumes the physical shape or identity of the old. Such replacements are called pseudomorphs. They are common with the copper carbonates in which malachite replaces azurite, often only in part, so that the crystal is part deep blue, part rich green (page 102). Brown limonite is found with the cubic shape of pyrite, which it has replaced, and it also is frequently found in the shape of a fossil, such as a clam. Opal from Australia often re-

places fossil shell, creating a natural gem (page 99). The gem tigerseye is a quartz pseudomorph after asbestos.

## Associations as Clues

Mineral associations can be major clues to mineral identities, for minerals are not distributed haphazardly in the earth. If you know the company a mineral keeps, you have two clues to its identity and where it may be found. The technical word for such mineral associations is paragenesis.

Most crystals are found in fissures and cavities in large rock masses. They have grown there from mineralized solutions that filled voids and caused changes in the rock itself. Metallic sulphides, such as pyrite, chalcopyrite, galena and the like, were deposited in this way, as well as quartz, calcite, siderite, barite and fluorite. Gold is usually found in quartz veins or nearby stream beds, or with silver minerals in copper sulphides, as at Bingham Canyon, Utah. Silver and lead, lead and zinc, and copper and iron minerals are often paired.

An example is the Tri-State district around Joplin, Mo. In its limestone beds galena and sphalerite were found, along with magnificent calcite crystals and such carbonates as cerussite and smithsonite. Here the limestone had been shattered by the Ozark uplift, allowing the mineralized solutions to enter. In a similar way the native copper was deposited in the basalts of the Michigan Upper peninsula, along with other copper minerals. Surface waters leach minerals from the rocks and as they percolate downward enrich deeper deposits. That is how the hydrous copper carbonates, azurite and malachite, originated in the Arizona mines, along with such beautiful minerals as wulfenite. Veins in any

50. Some minerals, such as this chrysoberyl sixling at left, form repeated twins which unite to make a ringlike pattern. The feldspar twins at right are, reading from left to right, Carlsbad, Manebach and Baveno types.

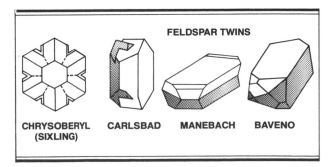

FELDSPAR TWINS

CHRYSOBERYL (SIXLING)    CARLSBAD    MANEBACH    BAVENO

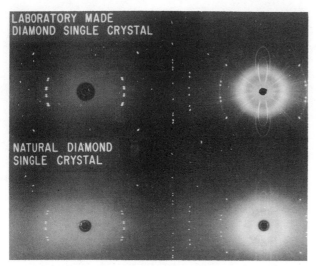

LABORATORY MADE
DIAMOND SINGLE CRYSTAL

NATURAL DIAMOND
SINGLE CRYSTAL

**51. X-ray diffraction patterns of natural and man-made diamonds show that both have the same atomic structure.**

mineralized rock may include vugs and other small cavities and fissures where crystals have had room to grow into perfect shape.

Two other types of rocks can be host to collectible crystals. As noted in the previous chapter, a hot igneous mass intruding a limestone or dolomite deposit may change it to marble. If the limestone or dolomite contains impurities of iron oxides, clay and quartz, the raw materials for a whole host of new minerals are present. Pyroxene draws calcium and magnesium from the dolomites and silicon and oxygen from the intruding mass. Likewise spinel and grossularite garnet may crystallize if clay is present to provide the aluminum. Other minerals likely to be found in an area of such contact metamorphism are graphite, tremolite, corundum, vesuvianite, scapolite and phlogopite mica.

Even more rewarding than the contact metamorphic rocks are the pegmatites, especially for the gem mineral collector. Pegmatites are associated with granites, and like them are made up primarily of quartz, feldspars and mica but in relatively large crystals. As an igneous mass cools, some gases and fluids that are slow to crystallize gather in voids. These include many rare elements, and from them crystallize the lithia minerals lepidolite and spodumene; the niobate-tantalate columbite; cassiterite, the major ore of tin; monazite, a phosphate of such rare metals as cerium, as well as beryl, which is our principal source of the metal beryllium.

Pegmatites include many rare phosphates. They are also home to such gems as emerald and aquamarine, tourmaline, kunzite, topaz and apatite, all of which will be discussed in the next chapter.

Striking examples of pegmatites have been found in Oxford County, Maine, and around Pala, California, as well as in North Carolina. Near Rumford, Maine, hundreds of pounds of gem and museum quality tourmaline were removed a few years ago from cavities in the Dunton mine, a presumably worked-out pegmatite. Not far away at North Groton, New Hampshire, the Palermo mine, worked for its feldspar and mica, has given science a score or more of rare phosphate minerals derived from alteration of a black mineral known as triphylite.

## Tests Used by Experts

Besides sight and simple physical tests, the professional mineralogist uses elaborate scientific tools in identifying minerals. A tiny crystal can be mounted on a slowly-revolving stand as the target of a beam of X-rays. Its atomic structure diffracts the rays onto a photographic film, creating a characteristic pattern (Figure 51). With the spectroscope, the color spectrum emitted by a hot sample of a mineral will reveal what elements compose it. Infra-red analysis of certain minerals is another useful tool of the professional. Still another involves the use of a polarizing microscope and refractometer to identify mineral components by their angles of refraction and variation in light absorption (page 114). Such professional methods, of course, call for an investment in equipment and training beyond the reach of most amateurs.

## Some Simple Chemical Tests

Chances are that you will be able to identify most common minerals by the simple physical tests outlined in previous paragraphs, and through the familiarity that comes from handling and studying representative specimens. If the color, luster, any cleavages, the shape of the crystals, and the matrix don't provide enough clues, try the hardness, streak and specific gravity tests. If you are still at a loss, there are some simple chemical tests you can try that do not require elaborate equipment or special skills. They are described in Appendix 2 and Table B.

## TABLE B MINERAL IDENTIFICATION CHART

| METALLIC LUSTER | COLOR | SPECIFIC GRAVITY | CRYSTAL FORM AND HABIT | ASSOCIATIONS | KEY TESTS (See Appendix 2) |
|---|---|---|---|---|---|
| **HARDNESS 1 TO 3** | | | | | |
| Molybdenite, $MoS_2$ Hardness 1-1.5 | Lead gray | 4.67-4.73 | Hexagonal, and flakes | Igneous rocks, pegmatites and quartz veins | Bluish gray streak on paper; greasy feel; oxidizing blowpipe flame gives yellow sublimate, bordered by white, which turns blue in reducing flame. |
| Graphite, C H. 1-2 | Black | 2.3 | Thin, hexagonal plates | Metamorphic rocks | Stains fingers; greasy feel; infusible and insoluble. |
| Covellite, CuS H. 1.5-2 | Blue, usually tarnished coppery color | 4.6-4.76 | Thin, hexagonal plates | With copper minerals | Flake burns with blue flame before melting. |
| Stibnite, $Sb_2S_3$ H.2 | Steel gray | 4.5-4.6 | Orthorhombic. Steely, slender crystals, often bent | With lead, iron and arsenic ore minerals | Melts very easily in oxidizing flame, giving white sublimate, edged with blue. |
| Chalcocite, $Cu_2S$ H. 2.5-3 | Lead gray | 7.2-7.4 | Orthorhombic. Commonly massive | With copper minerals | Responds to tests for copper; only gray copper sulphide; heavy. |
| Galena, PbS H. 2.5 | Lead gray | 7.4-7.6 | Isometric. Cubic or less commonly octahedral crystals | Segregations in limestone or igneous rocks; often with sphalerite | Perfect cubic cleavage; grey streak on paper. |
| Gold, Au H. 2.5-3 | Yellow to silvery yellow (from presence of silver) | 15.6-19.3 | Isometric. Octahedral crystals, usually wires or feathery | Quartz veins and placer deposits | Softer than other yellow minerals, and more malleable; very heavy. Non-magnetic. Won't tarnish. |
| Silver, Ag H. 2.5-3 | White, tarnishes black | 10.5 | Isometric, but usually wires or spray-like crystals | In ore veins with sulphides | Only malleable metal that dissolves in $HNO_3$. On addition of HCl, gives curdy precipitate that turns purple in sun. |
| Copper, Cu H. 3 | Copper red | 8.9 | Isometric. Distorted cubic or octahedral crystals, often arborescent | Ore veins and volcanic rocks | Malleable; only red metal; soluble in $HNO_3$; gives blue solution on addition of $NH_4OH$. |
| Bornite, $Cu_5FeS_4$ H. 3 | Bronzy, tarnishes purple | 5.06-5.08 | Usually massive. Isometric crystals rare | Copper veins, and sulphide ores. | "Peacock" iridescence when tarnished; fuses to magnetic ball on charcoal; gives copper test in $HNO_3$. |
| **HARDNESS 3.5-5.5** | | | | | |
| Chalcopyrite, $CuFeS_2$ H. 3.5-4 | Brassy to golden yellow | 4.1-4.3 | Tetragonal. Kite-shaped (sphenoidal) crystals | In veins with sulphide ores | Greenish black streak; softer, darker than pyrite; copper test also gives red (iron) precipitate. |
| Meteoric Iron, FeNi H. 4-5 | Rusty outside, steely inside | about 8 | Partly stone or all metal | In soil or craters | Magnetic; nickel test in $HNO_3$ solution; crystal figures on etched face. |

## TABLE B MINERAL IDENTIFICATION CHART (Continued)

| METALLIC LUSTER | COLOR | SPECIFIC GRAVITY | CRYSTAL FORM AND HABIT | ASSOCIATIONS | KEY TESTS |
|---|---|---|---|---|---|
| **HARDNESS 3.5 TO 5.5** | | | | | |
| Niccolite, NiAs H. 5-5.5 | Coppery color, tarnishes black | 7.78 | Massive or crusts | With silver ores and other arsenides | Under blowpipe gives off garlic fumes, fuses to bronzy globule; nickel test in $HNO_3$. |
| Chromite, $Cr_2O_4$ (MgFe) H. 5.5 | Black | 4.6 | Massive, rarely octahedral | Serpentine, and basic rocks | Streak brown;colors borax bead green; magnetic after being heated in reducing blowpipe flame. |
| **HARDNESS 6 AND OVER** | | | | | |
| Hematite, $Fe_2O_3$ H. 5.5-6.5 | Rusty red or black, often shiny scales or steely mass | 5.26 | Hexagonal. Fat rhombs, flat scales kidney-shaped and earthy masses | In all types of rocks. Colors soil red | Streak red; magnetic after heating under blowpipe. |
| Magnetite, $Fe_3O_4$ H. 6 | Black | 5.2 | Isometric. Often octahedrons or as grains | Igneous and metamorphic rocks, and heavy sands | Streak black; strongly magnetic. |
| Pyrite, $FeS_2$ H. 6-6.5 | Pale to brassy yellow | 5.02 | Cubes and pyritohedrons, often striated | In all types of rocks and in ore veins | Brittle; streak is greenish black; may contain gold; harder than most sulphides. |
| Marcasite, $FeS_2$ H. 6-6.5 | Pale to grayish yellow; often tarnished | 4.9 | Curved orthorhom-bic (coxcomb) crys-tals, or spearheads | Sedimentary rocks | More soluble than pyrite in cold $HNO_3$; usually paler than pyrite. |
| Pyrolusite, $MnO_2$ H.6 (crystals) | Steel gray, or soft, powdery black | 5.05 (crystals) 4.75 (massive) | Tetragonal. Fibrous crystal bundles; as dendrites in rocks | Manganese minerals | Streak black; gives off chlorine gas on dissolving in HCl; colors borax bead purple in oxidizing flame. |
| Rutile, $TiO_2$ H. 6-6.5 | Black, reddish in needles | 4.2-4.25 | Tetragonal. Striated prisms, or twins; capillary needles | Igneous and metamorphic rocks, and in sands | Light brown streak; powder boiled in dilute HCl with piece of zinc metal gives violet hue. |

| NON-METALLIC LUSTER | LUSTER | COLOR | SPECIFIC GRAVITY | CRYSTAL FORM AND HABIT | ASSOCIATIONS | KEY TESTS |
|---|---|---|---|---|---|---|
| **HARDNESS 1 TO 3** | | | | | | |
| Carnotite, hydrous potassium uranium vanadate H. 1 | Earthy | Brilliant yellow | 4.1 | Powdery | Sandstones; chief secondary uranium mineral | Non-fluorescent, but cold borax bead fluoresces green. |
| Talc, hydrous magnesium silicate H. 1 | Pearly, micaceous | White, light green, gray | 2.7-2.8 | Massive, as soapstone | Metamorphic rocks | Cleaves like mica; greasy feel. Used by tailors to mark cloth. |

## TABLE B MINERAL IDENTIFICATION CHART (Continued)

| NON-METALLIC LUSTER | LUSTER | COLOR | SPECIFIC GRAVITY | CRYSTAL FORM AND HABIT | ASSOCIATIONS | KEY TESTS |
|---|---|---|---|---|---|---|
| **HARDNESS 1 TO 3** | | | | | | |
| Bauxite, Al₂0₃.H₂0 (A mixture of minerals, all of which are hy-drated aluminum oxides) H. 1-3 | Dull | White to red brown | 2-2.5 | Claylike or small spheres | Sedimentary deposits of earthy alumi-num oxides | Colored blue when wet with cobalt nitrate under blowpipe. |
| Realgar, AₛS H. 1.5-2 | Resinous | Orange red | 3.5 | Usually massive | In ore veins with antimony sulphide | In reducing blow-pipe flame gives garlic odor and white sublimate. |
| Orpiment As₂S₃ H. 2 | Resinous | Yellowish orange | 3.5 | Monoclinic. Wedgelike crystals | With realgar | Waxy and mica-like. Fuses easily. |
| Sulphur, S H. 1.5-2.5 | Resinous | Light yellow to amber | 2.05-2.1 | Orthorhombic; brilliant, often translucent | Volcanic and sedimentary rocks | Melts easily, gives off choking fumes. |
| Gypsum, CaSO₄.2H₂O H. 2 | Pearly, glassy or silky | Light colors | 2.32 | Monoclinic. Tabular crystals of selenite, or silky fibers of satin spar | Sedimentary rocks, clay beds | Cleaves into thin plates; always feels smooth; soluble in hot diluted HCl but does not bubble. |
| Autunite, hydrous calcium uranium phosphate H. 2-2.5 | Pearly | Greenish to yellow | 3.1 | Orthorhombic. As thin flakes and crusts | In weathered uranium deposits and pegmatites | Brilliantly fluoresces green. |
| Chlorite, hydrous magnesium aluminum silicate (A family of minerals) H. 2-2.5 | Glassy or pearly | Dark green | 2.6-3.0 | Foliated or flaky. Penninite and clinochlore are chlorites | Schists and serpentines | Harder than talc; greener than any mica; flakes lack elasticity of mica. |
| Mica, family of complex silicates H. 2.5 on cleavage H. 4 on side of crystal. | Glassy or pearly | Muscovite, colorless or light; phlogo-pite, brown; biotite, black-brown; lepido-lite, lilac to yellow | 2.8-3.1 | Hexagonal. Perfect cleavage into flat sheets | Granites, schists and pegmatites. Muscovite usually in granite; phlogopite in metamorphosed limestone | Sheets flexible and spring back; mus-covite may show six-ray star pattern. |
| Halite, NaCl H. 2.5 | Glassy | Colorless, red or blue | 2.16 | Isometric | Dry flakes, sedimentary beds | Rock salt. Tastes salty. |
| Cinnabar, HgS H. 2.5 | Adamantine | Bright red | 8.1 | Usually as crust in volcanic regions, rock or crust | In veins | Volatilizes under blowpipe on charcoal; deposits metal when heated in closed tube. |

## TABLE B MINERAL IDENTIFICATION CHART (Continued)

| NON-METALLIC LUSTER | LUSTER | COLOR | SPECIFIC GRAVITY | CRYSTAL FORM AND HABIT | ASSOCIATIONS | KEY TESTS |
|---|---|---|---|---|---|---|
| **HARDNESS 1 TO 3** | | | | | | |
| Serpentine, hydrous magnesium silicate H. 2.5-4 | Resinous to silky | Light to dark green, yellow | 2.6 | Massive, verd antique marble is one form; chrysotile asbestos is another | Metamorphic rocks | White streak; smooth, greasy feel. Some varieties are fairly hard. |
| Calcite, $CaCO_3$ H. 3 | Glassy, pearly on cleavages | Colorless, light colors; | 2.7 | Hexagonal. Great variety but usually rhombs or scalenohedrons | All kinds of rocks except granites | Commonest soft, light mineral; cleaves perfectly to rhombs; if transparent may show double refraction; effervesces with dilute acid. |
| Vanadinite $Pb_5Cl(VO_4)_3$ H. 3 | Resinous | Red to brown | 6.5-7.0 | Hexagonal. Often barrel-shaped | In lead ore deposits | Melts easily. Stains HCl solution green. |
| Wulfenite $PbMoO_4$ H. 3 | Resinous | Yellow, orange to pale green | 6.5-7.0 | Tetragonal. Usually as tabular or paper-thin crystals | In lead deposits | Fuses to lead bead. Soluble in $H_2SO_4$. |
| **HARDNESS 3 TO 5** | | | | | | |
| Barite, $BaSO_4$ H. 3-3.5 | Glassy | Colorless, white, light blue | 4.5 | Orthorhombic. Tabular, often bladed, or as "roses" | Sedimentary rocks and sulphide ore veins | Heavy for light colored mineral; insoluble in acid. |
| Celestite, $SrSO_4$ H. 3-3.5 | Glassy | Colorless or light blue | 3.9-4.0 | Orthorhombic. Tabular or squarish crystals | Sedimentary rocks | Light blue hues in crystal; crimson by flame test. |
| Cerussite, $PbCO_3$ H. 3-3.5 | Adamantine | Colorless to gray | 6.55 | Orthorhombic, Crystal lattices and "V" twins | Oxidized lead ore zones | High luster and great weight; turns yellow, then red under gentle heat, then forms lead bead. |
| Azurite, $Cu_3(OH)_2(CO_3)_2$ H. 3.5-4 | Glassy | Bright to deep blue, used as gem. | 3.8 | Monoclinic. Prismatic crystals, often altered to malachite; or as crystal aggregates or massive | Copper ores | Only common deep blue mineral; gives copper test with $HNO_3$ and $NH_4OH$; effervesces in acid. |
| Malachite, $Cu_2(OH)_2CO_3$ H. 3.5-4 | Silky | Bright green, used as gem | 4.0 | Monoclinic. Usually massive or fibrous | Copper ores | Effervesces in HCl; gives copper test with $HNO_3$. |
| Dolomite, $CaMg(CO_3)_2$ H. 3.5-4 | Glassy to pearly | Often pink, also whitish | 2.85 | Hexagonal. Curved rhombs or massive. Ankerite is iron-rich form | Sedimentary rocks and low temperature ore veins | Cleaves like calcite; effervesces only in hot HCl or slowly if powdered. |

## TABLE B MINERAL IDENTIFICATION CHART (Continued)

| NON-METALLIC LUSTER | LUSTER | COLOR | SPECIFIC GRAVITY | CRYSTAL FORM AND HABIT | ASSOCIATIONS | KEY TESTS |
|---|---|---|---|---|---|---|
| **HARDNESS 3 TO 5** | | | | | | |
| Aragonite, CaCO₃ H. 3.5-4 | Glassy | White, light yellow | 2.9-3.0 | Orthorhombic. Needles, or twinned into "dollars"; or crusts, cave formations | Hot springs and caves and sedimentary rocks | Effervesces in acid; turns violet when powder is boiled in cobalt nitrate solution, whereas calcite stays white. |
| Cuprite, Cu₂0 H. 3.5-4 | Adamantine | Dark red | 6.14 | Isometric. Cubes, octahedrons or needle-like (chalcotrichite) | Copper ores | Fuses to copper bead under blow-pipe; copper test with HN0₃; red streak. |
| Rhodochrosite, MnC0₃ H 3.5-4 | Glassy | Rose pink, gray or brownish, used as gem | 3.4-3.6 | Hexagonal. Rhombs or massive | With manganese deposits and in metal ore veins | Cleaves like calcite; effervesces in hot acid. |
| Siderite, FeCO₃ H. 3.5-4 | Glassy | Milky brown or gray | 3.8-3.9 | Hexagonal. Rhombs like dolomite, or massive | Sedimentary rocks, iron ores | Cleaves like calcite; effervesces in hot acid; heavier than calcite. |
| Sphalerite, (ZnFe) S H. 3.5-4 | Resinous | Yellow brown, red, black | 3.9-4.1 | Isometric. Rounded and tetrahedral crystals | In all types of rock, and with sulphide ores | Under blowpipe gives charcoal coating yellow when hot that turns green with reducing flame and cobalt nitrate solution. |
| Stilbite, complex silicate H. 3.5-4 | Glassy to pearly | Yellow or reddish | 2.1-2.2 | Monoclinic. In bundles of crystals shaped like wheat shocks | One of the zeolites that grow in basalt and granite cavities | Swells under blow-pipe; pearly cleavage. |
| Fluorite, CaF₂ H. 4 | Glassy | Green, blue, yellow, purple, brown, colorless | 3.2 | Isometric. Cubes | Sedimentary rocks, ore veins | Perfect octahedral cleavage. Often fluorescent. |
| Colemanite, Ca₂B₆O₁₁. 5H₂O H. 4-4.5 | Glassy | Colorless | 2.4 | Monoclinic. Well formed crystals | Borax deposits | Flies apart under blowpipe and colors flame green; soluble in hot HCl with precipitate of borax flakes. |
| Scheelite, CaWO₄ H. 4.5-5 | Adamantine | White or reddish yellow | 5.9-6.1 | Tetragonal. Bipyramid crystals | Metamorphic zones in limestone | Fluoresces blue white in short wave ultraviolet. |

## TABLE B MINERAL IDENTIFICATION CHART (Continued)

| NON-METALLIC LUSTER | LUSTER | COLOR | SPECIFIC GRAVITY | CRYSTAL FORM AND HABIT | ASSOCIATIONS | KEY TESTS |
|---|---|---|---|---|---|---|
| **HARDNESS 3 TO 5** | | | | | | |
| Smithsonite, $ZnCO_3$ H. 4.5 | Glassy to greasy | Blue, dull brown, or earthy (dry bone) | 4.3-4.4 | Hexagonal. Botryoidal or crusts | Oxidized zone of sulphide ore veins | Effervesces in HCl; heated fragment, touched with cobalt nitrate and reheated, gives a green color; hardest of the carbonates. |
| Turquoise, a hydrous copper and aluminum phosphate H. 4-5 | Waxy | Green to blue, used as gem | 2.6-3.0 | Usually in seams | Nodules in phosphate rocks | Often waxed and dyed for jewelry. |
| Apatite, $Ca_5(Cl,F,OH)(PO_4)_3$ H. 5 | Glassy to oily | Colorless, brown, blue, green or yellow | 3.1-3.2 | Hexagonal. Variety of crystal habits, often appear melted | Igneous rocks, pegmatites | Melts on edge of chip and colors flame reddish yellow. |
| **HARDNESS 5 TO 7** | | | | | | |
| Goethite, $FeO(OH)$ H. 5-5.5 | Silky | Black or dark brown | 4.28 | Orthorhombic. Fibrous and radiating, or stalactitic | With other iron minerals | Yellowish streak; gives off water in closed tube; magnetic after heating. |
| Datolite $Ca(OH)(BSiO_4)$ H. 5.5 | Glassy in crystals porcelain like - in massive | Crystals colorless; massive red, green, white | 2.8-3.0 | Usually in basalt with zeolites; massive from Michigan copper mines | Monoclinic or massive | Fuses to white mass, then bead. |
| Opal, $SiO_2.nH_2O$ H. 5-6 | Glassy | Colorless or light; when it shows play of colors (opalescence) it is used as gem | 1.9-2.2 | Amorphous, or fossil forms | Hot springs, volcanic and sedimentary rocks | Often fluorescent; gives off water in closed tube. |
| Augite, magnesium, calcium silicate with iron and aluminum. A pyroxene H. 5-6 | Glassy to dull | Gray green to black | 3.2-3.4 | Monoclinic. Stubby, eight-sided crystals | Commonest of rock-forming pyroxenes | Pale green streak; has nearly 90 degree cleavage so that flakes have rectangular cross section, like all pyroxenes. |
| Hornblende, iron, magnesium, calcium silicate. An amphibole. H. 5-6 | Glassy, especially on cleavage | Dark green to black | 3.2 | Monoclinic. Prisms. Uralite and byssolite are amphiboles | Metamorphic and igneous rocks | More lustrous than augite; amphiboles cleave at 56 and 124 degrees, and flakes have wedge shape. |

## TABLE B MINERAL IDENTIFICATION CHART (Continued)

| NON-METALLIC LUSTER | LUSTER | COLOR | SPECIFIC GRAVITY | CRYSTAL FORM AND HABIT | ASSOCIATIONS | KEY TESTS |
|---|---|---|---|---|---|---|
| **HARDNESS 5 TO 7** | | | | | | |
| Actinolite, complex silicate. An amphibole. H. 5-6 | Glassy | White, green or violet. Nephrite jade is gem | 3-3.2 | Monoclinic. Well-formed long crystals in masses | Metamorphosed limestone, schists, gneiss | Splinters fuse with difficulty. Asbestos is a variety. |
| Diopside, $CaMg(SiO_3)_2$ A pyroxene. H. 5-6 | Glassy | White, light green, brown | 3.2-3.38 | Monoclinic. Well-formed prisms in marble | Metamorphosed limestone | Light green color. |
| Kyanite, $Al_2SiO_5$ H. 5 along crystal and 7 across | Glassy | Blue and green | 3.6-3.7 | Triclinic. Masses of long blades | Schist and gneiss | Unique variation in hardness; splintery fracture. |
| Willemite, $Zn_2SiO_4$ H. 5.5 | Resinous | White, green, yellow, blue. Troostite is a brown form | 3.9-4.2 | Hexagonal. Usually massive | Zinc veins, and at Franklin, N.J., in metamorphic rocks | Often fluorescent; chip dipped in $Na_2CO_3$ fuses in blowpipe flame to brown enamel, which turns green when drop of cobalt nitrate is applied and it is reheated. |
| Rhodonite, $(MnFeCa)SiO_3$ H. 5.5-6 | Glassy | Pink to gray; weathering blackens exposed surface. Used as gem | 3.58-3.7 | Triclinic. Short prisms, usually massive | Metamorphic rocks | Splintery fracture; fuses to brown glass under blowpipe; does not react with acid as rhodochrosite does and Is much harder than rhodochrosite. |
| Sodalite, sodium aluminum silicate with chlorine H. 5.5-6 | Glassy | Colorless or pink, but usually blue | 2.2-2.3 | Isometric. Usually massive | Igneous rocks, low in silicate | Pink variety (hackmanite) is fluorescent; heated in blowpipe fluoresces orange (long wave) and blue (short wave). |
| Feldspar, aluminum silicates with potassium, sodium or calcium H. 6 *(See Notes) | Glassy to pearly | White, pink, red, green, yellow, gray or dark gray | 2.5-2.76 | Boxy crystals. Orthoclase is monoclinic; all other feldspars are triclinic | Igneous and metamorphic rocks | Pearly cleavages form the bright spots in granites; plagioclase feldspars are usually twinned and show fine striations on cleavage faces. |
| Jadeite, $NaAlSi_2O_6$ H. 6.5 | Glassy | White, mauve, brown, yellow, green, imperial green, orange, lavender, red | 3.25 | Monoclinic, massive | Metamorphic rocks rich in sodium minerals | Tough, harder than serpentine; jadeite is more granular than nephrite jade. |

## TABLE B MINERAL IDENTIFICATION CHART (Continued)

| NON-METALLIC LUSTER | LUSTER | COLOR | SPECIFIC GRAVITY | CRYSTAL FORM AND HABIT | ASSOCIATIONS | KEY TESTS |
|---|---|---|---|---|---|---|
| **HARDNESS 5 TO 7** | | | | | | |
| Prehnite, hydrous calcium silicate aluminum H. 6-6.5 | Oily to glassy | Light green or white | 2.8-2.9 | Orthorhombic. Usually botryoidal, ridged with curving crystal edges | With zeolites in basalt | Fuses under blowpipe and swells to brown glass. |
| Cassiterite, $SnO_2$ H. 6-7 | Adamantine when in crystals | Yellow, red-brown, black | 6.8-7.1 | Bipyramid crystals, wood-like crusts, or greasy gray gravel (wood tin) | Pegmatites, placers | Very heavy; light colored streak; placed in dilute HCl with piece of zinc, it develops shiny coating of tin. |
| Epidote, complex silicate H. 6-7 | Glassy | Pistachio to dark green | 3.35-3.45 | Monoclinic. Thin, grooved prisms, or tiny crystals (druses) | In metamorphic and some igneous rocks | Transparent crystal changes color, as it is turned, from green to brown. |
| Spodumene, $LiAlSi_2O_6$ H. 6.5-7 | Glassy | Lavender to pink is gem kunzite, green is liddenite | 3.1-3.2 | Monoclinic. Usually as long crystals | Pegmatites | Colors flame red; tough splintery fracture. |
| Zircon, $ZrSiO_4$ H. 6.5-7 | Adamantine | Brown, gray, colorless, used as gem | 4.-4.7 | Tetragonal. Square prisms with pyramid terminations | In granites and sands | Commonly fluoresces orange; crystal shape distinctive. Heated to blue or colorless gem. |
| Olivine, $(Mg, Fe)_2 SiO_4$ H. 6.5-7 | Glassy to oily | Olive green; crystals more bottle green. Used as gem | 3.27-3.37 | Orthorhombic. Usually in granular masses | Dark lavas | Slowly soluble in HCl; color is characteristic. Peridot is gem form. |
| Garnet, silicates of calcium, aluminum, iron, chromium, etc. H. 6.5-7.5* *(See Notes) | Glassy | Red, green, orange, brown, black | 3.5-4.3 | Isometric. Ball-like crystals | All kinds of rocks, especially schists | Most varieties fuse readily; crystal form distinctive. |
| **HARDNESS 7 AND OVER** | | | | | | |
| Quartz, $SiO_2$ H. 7 *(See Notes) | Glassy | Colorless, gray, amethyst, rose, brown | 2.65 | Hexagonal. Six-sided prisms with pyramid terminations | In light colored rocks | Crystals often striated across prism; conchoidal fracture; crystal shape. |
| Tourmaline, complex boron, fluorine silicate H. 7-7.5 | Glassy | Green, blue, red, black, often in zones; used as gem | 3.0-3.2 | Hexagonal. Crystals long and striated lengthwise with rounded triangular cross section | Pegmatites and igneous and metamorphic rocks | Striations and rounded triangular shape of crystal cross section. |

## TABLE B MINERAL IDENTIFICATION CHART (Continued)

| NON-METALLIC LUSTER | LUSTER | COLOR | SPECIFIC GRAVITY | CRYSTAL FORM AND HABIT | ASSOCIATIONS | KEY TESTS |
|---|---|---|---|---|---|---|
| **HARDNESS 7 AND OVER** | | | | | | |
| Staurolite, hydrous iron, aluminum silicate H. 7 | Resinous to dull | Dark brown | 3.6-3.7 | Orthorhombic. Six-sided flat crystals, often twinned | In schists and gneiss | Twinning at 60 and 90 degree angles; shape and color. |
| Beryl, $Be_3Al_2Si_6O_{18}$ H. 7.5-8 | Glassy | Emerald green, aquamarine blue, heliodor, yellow, morganite pink, goshenite, colorless | 2.75 | Hexagonal prisms | Pegmatites | Crystal shape and hardness. |
| Spinel, $MgAl_2O_4$ H. 8 | Glassy | A family of wide variety of colors. Red used as gem | 3.5-4.0 | Isometric. Usually octahedral. Gahnite is a variety. Magnetite is an iron spinel, franklinite an iron-zinc spinel | In contact metamorphic limestones | Crystal form and hardness. |
| Topaz, $Al_2(OHF)$ $(SiO_4)$ H. 8 | Glassy | Rich orange, blue, yellow and pink. Used as gem | 3.5 | Orthorhombic. Stubby crystals, brittle, cleave parallel to base | In pegmatites and other granites and rhyolites | Cleavage and insolubility. |
| Chrysoberyl, $BeAl_2O_4$ H. 8.5 | Glassy | Yellowish green. Alexandrite is green changing to red; catseye has sharp moving line in stone | 3.71 | Orthorhombic tabular, often twinned or sixlings | In pegmatites, mica schists | Great hardness, optical effects, insoluble. |
| Corundum, $Al_2O_3$ H. 9 | Adamantine 6-rayed star gems | Ruby red, sapphire blue, and other colors | 4.02 | Hexagonal prisms, often bipyramids or plates | Igneous and metamorphic rocks | Great hardness, high specific gravity; crystal shape distinctive. |
| Diamond, C H.10 | Adamantine | Colorless, blue-white, yellow, brown, green, red, blue | 3.5 | Isometric, rounded and distorted octahedrons | In volcanic pipes and alluvial deposits | Great hardness, brilliance |

### NOTES

Among the crystal forms of quartz are rock crystal, amethyst, yellow citrine, rose and smoky quartz or cairngorm, and forms with inclusions such as sagenite, filled with fine needles, moss agate with dendritic patterns, and aventurine with tiny mica inclusions. The chalcedony forms are agate, green bloodstone or heliotrope with red dots, red-hued carnelian, green chrysoprase, blue chrysocolla, striped tigerseye, petrified wood and bone, flint, chert and jasper.

Gem forms of garnet are ruby red pyrope, purplish red almandine, orange and brown-red spessartite, grossularite green, reddish brown or yellow; andradite, green or black, and rhodolite, a violet red mixture of pyrope and almandine. Demantoid garnet, a rare green form, is an andradite garnet; a green spessartite is often called Transvaal jade.

The feldspars fall into two rock forming groups — the potassium feldspars, orthoclase and microcline; and the plagioclase feldspars, mixtures of albite and anorthite which include oligoclase, andesine, labradorite and bytownite. Amazonite is a green microcline. Sanidine is a glassy form of orthoclase from which moonstones are cut.

Flashing perthite and glistening sunstone are other gem forms of the feldspar minerals.

## Chapter IV

# Gems—the Flowers of the Mineral Kingdom

*"Nature never put her jewels into a garret."*
—Francis Bacon

Together we have talked about earth's skeletal foundation, the rocks, and the minerals of which they are composed. Some of these minerals are valued by man for industrial uses and some for their rarity, color or crystal perfection. But none are valued as highly as the select group we call gems, precious minerals most of them, and the aristocrats of their kind.

Some materials used for jewelry, such as amber and pearl, are not minerals, but most gems come from minerals that give them the qualities important in a gem. The first quality is, of course, a unique beauty. The glory of rubies, sapphires and emeralds lies in their intense, vivid colors. The diamond is king of gems for its ability to break up light into flashing prisms. The opal is incomparable for its glowing inner flames, and the star stones have a magic all their own.

Ideally, a gem should also be hard enough to resist the abrasion to which a ring or pin is subject. Quartz is one of the most prevalent minerals on earth; dust contains a certain amount of it. A gem will grow dull if it is not as hard or harder than quartz, as most gems are. Some that are softer than quartz, such as opal, moonstone and turquoise, must be repolished occasionally. But these, like lapis lazuli and malachite, are so attractive for their color or tricks with light that they remain popular gems despite their inferior hardness.

A gem should also be relatively durable, not likely to cleave, split or crack under normal use. Garnets are brittle and anyone who has a garnet ring or brooch that grandmother wore may notice that the stones show signs of chipping on the facets. So garnet, as well as opal and many of the feldspar gems, should be protected as much as possible by proper mountings.

For transparent gems such as rubies or emeralds to be valuable, the color must not be too light or too dark, the gem must have clarity and be free of obvious flaws, and it must be cut to bring out all of its radiance.

All of the gems we have named are prized but if the streets were paved with diamonds and rubies, who would bother to pick one up? Rarity lends enchantment; what few can own many will desire, and a fortunate few will cherish. It is no accident that kings and queens are crowned with the gem treasures of their kingdoms. Rarity, however, is a paradoxical quality. If a gem mineral is too rare to be widely known, and never gets into the jewelry stores, it never becomes fashionable and remains the secret darling of a few mineralogists. They don't set the fashions in jewelry. Benitoite is one example. It is found in only one place, San Benito County, California, and only a small proportion of its wedge-shaped crystals are of gem quality. Yet benitoite rivals sapphire in color and could rival it in popularity if it were not so rare. Another example is gem quality andalusite, which resembles pink or green tourmaline but is much rarer. Chiastolite, the mineral that shows a cross-shaped pattern, is a more common form of andalusite. Only some 100 of the 2,500 known minerals have even a few of the qualities desirable for a gem. Of these, it is rare to see more than 15 represented in a jeweler's stock.

Rarity and beauty placed amethyst among the most eagerly sought-after gem stones less than two centuries ago. Then discovery of vast deposits in South America quickly robbed amethyst of much of its value. If a similar discovery of emeralds were made tomorrow, one of our most costly gems would suffer a like fate. Imagine emerald rings at a few dollars a carat!

Fashion also influences the desirability of gems. There have been years when yellow gems were preferred; others when green stones were worn by social leaders. A striking example exists in the recent vogue of massive "Indian" turquoise jewelry that real Indians would consider ostentatious.

## Gems in Ancient Times

"Love of precious stones is deeply implanted in the human heart," wrote George Frederick Kunz. Gems are found in the ruins of Babylonia; in the tombs of Egyptian rulers and Chinese princes as far back as the dawn of civilization. American Indians made use of more than 80 ornamental stones, more than were known to the Europeans who first came to America. The Indians used them for ornaments, weapons, mirrors, abrasives and as totems in medicine and worship. Chalcedony, jasper, obsidian, moss agate, azurite, jade, turquoise, amber, and garnet were among the favorites, Native children in Brazil played with diamonds, and the Toltecs worked gems and put them in gold mountings.

Ancient man in the Middle East cut beautiful seals, amulets and scarabs in hard stones and endowed gems with magical powers to cure the sick and protect the wearer. Perhaps through such beliefs came the first use of gems as personal ornaments. Jewels were prescribed like medicine; green ones to improve the sight, red ones to check bleeding or make a warrior invulnerable. If your ring grew dull, you were becoming ill; take some powdered stone as medicine.

The Renaissance brought more rational views, but even today some trace of this association of persons with gemstones remains in the birthstone list. This list goes back only to the 18th century, but it is perhaps more popular and widely recognized today than in any previous age. The list varies somewhat from country to country, but the one generally used in the United States is:

| | |
|---|---|
| January—Garnet | July—Ruby |
| February—Amethyst | August—Sardonyx |
| March—Bloodstone | September—Sapphire |
| April—Diamond | October—Opal |
| May—Emerald | November—Topaz |
| June—Pearl | December—Turquoise |

In England aquamarine is the March stone and August is peridot.

Ancient people named gems by their color, so that it is often impossible to interpret their terms into modern phraseology. Sapphirus, for example, apparently was the term used for any blue stone and specifically for lapis lazuli. Garnets and spinels were often called rubies or carbuncles. Peridots were confused with emeralds. Even the Bible's 125 Greek and Hebrew names for gems have exhausted the talents and patience of translators.

Amateurs interested in gems have a wider outlook than the commercial jeweler. They would like to have a stock of rubies and diamonds, too, and sometimes they find such precious jewels. But they can also be happy with the more abundant gems, such as agate, jasper, and the feldspars.

## Diamonds in America

Nothing epitomizes the appeal of gems more aptly than the diamond. What other object on earth could be so small and yet so beautiful and valuable, and retain its worth for countless generations? Given such an appeal, it is surprising how many diamond discoveries have been accidental. It was the search for gold that first brought to light the occurrence of diamonds in the United States. The greasy-looking crystals stayed in the pan with gold and black sand. Several hundred were found in placer mining operations in the Mother Lode region of California, including a few as large as six carats. Diamonds were found in the same way in Georgia and North Carolina. Diamonds brought down by glaciers from Canada turned up for gold hunters in Indiana streams. Several big ones were found near Milwaukee, Wisconsin, such as the Eagle diamond of 15.5 carats, found by a well digger, and the 21.25 carat Theresa diamond.

But the Mecca for diamond hunters lies a few miles southeast of Murfreesboro, Arkansas, in a 78-acre tract now part of the Crater of Diamonds state park, which is open to collectors for a small fee. Some 100,000 diamonds have been found

**52. A 340 carat, faceted Russian aquamarine from the Hope collection is posed in front of an even larger aquamarine crystal. Large, flawless aquamarine crystals have been found frequently; sizable emeralds are rare.**

here in the four volcanic "pipes", which are geologically like those in which diamonds occur in the great South African fields. The largest Arkansas find is the Uncle Sam of 40.23 carats, and several others larger than 10 carats have rewarded the patient search and sharp eyes of amateurs. The diamond-bearing ground in the state park is bulldozed frequently to provide fresh soil for the thousands who search there.

Diamond is carbon, like the graphite in a lead pencil, but its crystal structure is so dense that it is the hardest substance in nature. On the conventional Mohs scale it is rated 10, one step above corundum at 9, but in an actual abrasion test it would rate 42 to corundum's 9. Diamond's beauty lies in its ability to refract or bend and reflect back light so that it flashes with many colors. Refractive index is a measure of this power. On this scale diamond stands 2.42 to ruby's 1.77 and emerald's 1.58 (Table C).

India supplied most of the famous diamonds of history until the Brazilian and South African fields were discovered in the last century. More recently Siberia has become an important source. Commonly found as octahedrons, diamonds also assume the shape of cubes or dodecahedrons, all of which forms are consistent with its crystal structure. Absence of color ranks high among qualities considered in evaluating diamonds, but yellow stones are not uncommon

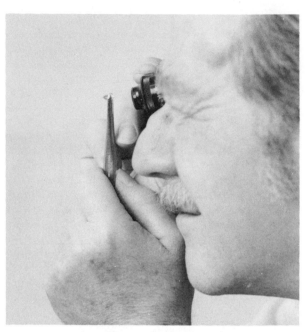

53. To check diamond for undesirable trace of color, look through the girdle or widest part in clear northern light. To check for flaws, look through top (crown) and bottom (pavilion) with a 10-power magnifier.

## TABLE C INDICES OF REFRACTION OF MAJOR GEMSTONES

The brilliance or sparkle of a gem depends on its ability to refract light when properly cut. The index of refraction of the gem is a measure of this potential, with higher numbers representing more brilliance.

| GEM | INDEX OF REFRACTION |
| --- | --- |
| Rutile | 2.61 |
| Diamond | 2.42 |
| Zircon | 1.94 |
| Andradite garnet | 1.89 |
| Uvarovite garnet | 1.87 |
| Spessartite garnet | 1.80 |
| Ruby, sapphire | 1.77 |
| Chrysoberyl | 1.75 |
| Grossular garnet | 1.73 |
| Spinel* | 1.72 |
| Pyrope garnet | 1.71 |
| Peridot | 1.69 |
| Topaz | 1.63 |
| Tourmaline* | 1.62 |
| Emerald, aquamarine | 1.58 |
| Quartz | 1.54 |
| Opal* | 1.44 |

*Variable

and brown, blue, green and red diamonds are a connoisseur's treasures.

A famous fancy diamond is the blue Hope diamond of 45.5 carats now in the Natural History museum of the Smithsonian Institution in Washington, D.C. This gem is said to be the one brought by Jean Baptiste Tavernier from India and purchased by King Louis XIV of France. It was stolen with the other French crown jewels during the Revolution in 1792, recut to disguise it, and sold in London in 1830 to Henry Philip Hope, a banker. On his death a few years later it was sold, passed through several hands, and finally was bought by a New York dealer, Harry Winston. He gave it to the museum in 1958, where it is on display. A diamond even deeper blue than the Hope, however, is the 31-carat, heart-shaped Eugenie Blue (page 73).

The Tiffany diamond of 128.5 carats, which is owned and displayed by the New York jewelers of that name, is remarkable for its rich canary yellow color. Largest of the green diamonds is the Dresden of 41 carats, once a proud possession of the ruling family of Saxony, and displayed in their former palace in Dresden, located in communist East Germany.

Aside from such rare stones, the most desirable diamond is one that shows no trace of color, especially yellow, when viewed from the side through the girdle or widest part in a clear northern light (Figure 53). Absence of flaws visible under a 10-power glass, clarity, and proper cutting to bring out maximum dispersion also enter into evaluation of a cut diamond (see Chapter Nine). As the poet James Thomson wrote,

How from the diamond singles out each ray,
Where all, though trembling with 10,000
    hues,
Effuse one dazzling undivided light.

Larger stones are rarer than small; a diamond of three carats will bring substantially more than three one-carat stones (Figure 54).

Despite their attractiveness, diamonds would probably not bring as high prices as they do if the supply was not controlled by the DeBeers syndicate, which also stimulates the demand by promoting diamond as the engagement ring stone. Some huge diamonds have been found; the largest, the Cullinan weighed 3,106 carats, nearly 1⅓ pounds. The stone was 4 x 2½ x 1½ inches. From it were cut two gems, of 516.5 and 309.5 carats, that are among the British crown jewels. Illegal possession of rough diamonds is a serious offense in South Africa. A flight doctor stationed in the Gold Coast in World War II, however, was allowed to buy some rough diamonds from the natives by the U.S. Army provost marshal, who was trying to keep them out of the hands of Germans buying on the black market for use in war production tools in Germany. A veteran mineral collector, he said he fought the war with a magnifying glass in one hand, a scalpel in the other.

About 20 per cent of the rough diamonds are of gem grade, the others go into industrial uses such as abrasive materials, and metal-turning tools. Most gemstones are cut to the brilliant shape, but emerald cut, marquise and some other styles are popular (page 68). All are shaped with the same machinery. If necessary, the rough stone is cleaved along a cleavage plane to eliminate a defect, or sawed to shape with a metal blade impregnated with diamond dust. The stone is then bruted—rounded by pressure against a revolving diamond. It is then faceted on a rotating metal wheel, called a dop, which is spread with diamond dust and oil, as explained in Chapter Nine.

## Rubies and Sapphires

The ruby and sapphire are essentially identical except in color. Both are corundum, which is aluminum oxide. Ruby is red; sapphire is blue or any color of corundum except deep red. Burma is the home of the coveted and costly purplish "pi-

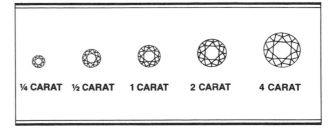

¼ CARAT    ½ CARAT    1 CARAT    2 CARAT    4 CARAT

54. **How carat sizes in diamonds compare. In the same carat sizes, heavier rubies and sapphires would be smaller, lighter emeralds would be larger.**

geon's blood red" ruby (page 74). There deeply buried gravel beds are worked by hand for ruby and other precious stones. The gem trade gets most of its supply, however, from Ceylon (Sri Lanka) and Thailand.

"Corn-flower blue" sapphires from Kashmir, India, set the standard for that gem, but Australia and Ceylon contribute their share. The golden orange hue is especially beautiful (page 75). Australian sapphires often have streaks of green in them. Such parti-colors are characteristic of corundum, and also of amethyst.

Ruby of the most desirable color and quality, especially in multi-carat sizes, is the most costly of all gemstones. A 10-carat ruby, for example, would bring $10,000 a carat. Blue sapphire is less expensive, although it has risen in price and favor in recent years. A fine sapphire would be priced at several thousand dollars a carat. A fancy-colored sapphire's value depends primarily on fashion as well as quality. Both ruby and sapphire occasionally exhibit the phenomenon called asterism, such as the 138-carat Rosser Reeves star ruby in the Smithsonian Institution (page 74), and the 563-carat Star of India sapphire in the American Museum of Natural History. Reflection of light from symmetrically-arranged inclusions causes a six-rayed star to appear in the translucent stone.

Colored stones are cut to enhance the color of the stone; a dense one would be cut thinner than a light-colored one, with the best color placed in the bottom of the stone, because color rather than dispersion is the desired quality (Figure 55). Corundum is heavier than diamond, with a specific gravity of 4.03 to diamond's 3.52 and emerald's 2.74. For this reason, if the three stones were cut to identical weights, the ruby or sapphire would be smaller than the diamond, and the diamond would be smaller than the emerald (Figure 54).

Corundum gems have long been mined from gravel beds north of Franklin, North Carolina, where amateur collectors work at flumes full of

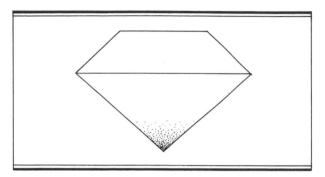

**55.** Where color is weak or variable, placing the most desirable color zone in the bottom of the stone insures the best color dispersion.

rushing water. Here they can wash bucketsful of muddy gravel sold to them by the local mine operators. Good to fair stones turn up in the gravel, a few of gem quality. Near Franklin is a house built on a foundation of local rubies and sapphires. A company mining the corundum gravels of Cowee Creek went out of business, leaving an employe with a warehouse containing buckets of ruby and sapphire that were not of gem quality. He built a house nearby and mixed the crystals into the concrete for its foundation. His daughter, who lives in the place, says that occasionally she has to shoo away eager rockhounds bent on digging out a few specimens.

Flat gem sapphires are found near Helena, Montana, but the best American sapphires have been mined from Yogo Gulch, in Judith Basin County, Montana. Long operated by an English syndicate, the mine there has been opened to amateurs in recent years. The Yogo Gulch sapphires lack the depth of color of the best oriental gems. But they have been in demand because they are more attractive for evening wear under artificial light than darker sapphires.

### Weight Measurements

Since weight is an important element in a gem's value, knowledge of the system for estimating it is of interest. Valuable gems are sold by the carat, which is one-fifth of a gram. An ounce contains 28.3 grams. For diamonds, weight is expressed in carats and points, a point being 1/100th of a carat. A diamond, then, might weigh 1 carat, 24 points, which is written as a decimal, 1.24 carats. A paper clip weighs about three carats, an office size staple about 17 points. Relatively common gems of good quality and rarer ones of poor quality are usually sold by the gram. Agate and jasper are sold by the pound, or the kilogram, which is 2¼ pounds.

Pearls are valued by the grain, which is one-fourth of a carat.

### Emeralds and Aquamarines

In value, emerald dominates the beryl family to which it belongs (see page 73). A fashionable member of the beryl family, aquamarine, is found in huge, almost flawless crystals, (one weighing 229 pounds was found in Brazil in 1910). But large emerald crystals of gem quality are exceedingly rare. The Devonshire emerald of 1,384 carats is in the British Museum. The Spanish conquerers of South America sent back to Europe many large emeralds from the mines in Colombia that were absorbed into royal collections. Ancient stones came from Egypt; Cleopatra wore emeralds from there. Fine emeralds from Ekaterinberg in the Ural mountains of Siberia adorned beauties of the Russian imperial court. According to one well authenticated story, all emeralds from the royal lapidary works at Ekaterinburg were reserved for the court, but several were smuggled to Germany and sold to a prince whose wife wore them to a reception at the Russian court. They were recognized as Russian emeralds; the intrigue was discovered, and the director of the cutting works was put in prison.

An emerald figures in an even more curious recent recognition story. According to Paul Desautels of the Smithsonian Institution, a guest at a White House reception for Queen Elizabeth was about to be introduced to the Queen when she noticed that the Queen was wearing an emerald inferior to the one the guest had on her finger. To avoid embarrassment, she turned the stone so that it was hidden, never wore it again, and put it in a safety box from which it was taken several years later to be given to the Smithsonian. Harry Winston, the New York jeweler who saw the gem at the time, said the stone had come from one of a pair of earrings that had belonged to the Russian empress Catherine.

Excellent emerald crystals of magnificent color have been found in Alexander County, North Carolina, near the mines from which came the green spodumene known as hiddenite, named for the superintendent of the mine. Some of variable quality come from near Little Switzerland, North Carolina. Fine crystals as well as necklaces made from North Carolina stones are in the Smithsonian. A congressman from Alexander County once urged the state legislature to put a railroad through the region, saying that "up there in Alexander County we have precious stones so valuable that a June bug can carry a fortune on its back." That is how North Carolina got the June bug railroad.

Brazilian mines have yielded a quantity of gem emerald, most of it lighter in color than the Colombian emerald, and its mines supply the world with aquamarine from the pegmatite dikes of Minas Gerais state. Blue and brilliant, aquamarine has become one of the most popular gems of our time. Stoneham, Maine, is recognized as the source of some of the finest aquamarine found in this country. A 133-carat gem from that locality is a prized exhibit at the Field Museum of Natural History in Chicago. In addition, Maine has produced some excellent golden beryl.

Among all the strange localities where man has gone for precious stones perhaps none is stranger than 14,000-foot-high, stormy Mt. Antero in Colorado. Here daring amateurs have discovered cavities near the summit containing aquamarines of deep color, as well as crystals of phenacite, an almost colorless gem.

Beryl is a silicate of beryllium and aluminum; chrysoberyl is an oxide of the same metals and is a trifle harder than its cousin. In addition, it has provided the gem lexicon with two exotic members, catseye and alexandrite.

56. This Chalmers topaz from Brazil weighs 5280 carats and its blue color resembles aquamarine. Green and red topazes are occasionally found in Brazil.

While other minerals, such as quartz and tourmaline, occasionally exhibit the effect known as chatoyancy, white stripe like that reflected by a cat's eye, none provides such rare and perfect examples as chrysoberyl. Its honey hue is broken by a sharp milk-white eye (see discussion page 69). For a fine example $1,000 or more a carat is asked. Brazil, Burma and Ceylon are sources. Rarer yet is another chrysoberyl, the alexandrite. It was named for Czar Alexander II of Russia because the gem was discovered on his birthday in 1891 and in Russia, from which the best examples have come. Alexandrite's uniqueness lies in a delicate color balance which makes it a purplish red in incandescent light and a bluish green in daylight. Ceylon and Burma are other sources.

## Tourmaline, an American Gem

Tourmaline enjoys the distinction of being the chameleon stone, for it occurs in nearly every color of the rainbow and could masquerade as most of the rarer gems. Not only is it colorless, blue, green, red, brown and black, but it is frequently bicolored, with the pencil-like crystal perhaps pink on the end, then a zone of blue, then a zone of green (page 77). Or it may be zoned across the crystal like a slice of watermelon, green on the surface, red inside.

Tourmaline is really a family of minerals. The lithium-rich variety of this complex borosilicate is called elbaite, and is subdivided into rubellite (red), indicolite (blue), achroite (colorless) and green, the commonest color. The other varieties—buergerite, dravite and schorl—are usually too dark to cut, although Ceylon and Upper New York State have some brown dravite of good quality.

The jewelry trade has slowly begun to give tourmaline the place it deserves. Comparatively plentiful, it displays vivid deep greens and robust reds, and the bicolors and watermelon types are unique. Tourmaline also ranks second to chrysoberyl among catseye fanciers.

Tourmaline has a strong claim to being the American gem, for two of the localities that first brought it to attention are in Maine and California. The Maine discovery has been recounted in a previous chapter, and since then a ton or more of crystals, many of gem quality, have been taken from a series of pockets in a pegmatite near Rumford, called the Dunton mine. Several mines near Pala, California, worked early in the century and reopened within the last ten years, have yielded some of the largest and finest crystal specimens in the world. Much of the world's supply of tourmaline, especially green, has come from Brazil. Some of it could be mistaken for emerald, though tourmaline's specific gravity is higher than emerald's (3 to 3.2 versus 2.6 to 2.8).

### Topaz

Topaz, like tourmaline, assumes a variety of colors, although the name is usually associated with yellow stones. So common is this that jewelers often sell yellow quartz (citrine) as topaz, quartz topaz or Rio Grande topaz, and even yellow corundum is labeled oriental topaz.

Lively, golden-brown topaz is highly desirable, and stones free of cleavage flaws and inclusions will sell for several hundred dollars a carat. Some yellow stones when heated will turn pink and are marketed as pink topaz. Fine blue topaz is easily mistaken for fine aquamarine, and green and red topaz are occasionally mined in Brazil, the major source. Colorless or pale topaz crystals weighing hundreds of pounds are among the marvels shown in museums (Figure 56).

Classic blue and green topaz crystals came from the Ural mountains in Siberia and more recently from Rhodesia, Ceylon, Burma, Mason County, Texas, and the Pike's Peak area in Colorado. Mexico and the Thomas mountains in Utah supply beautiful sherry-colored crystal groups, unfortunately usually too small for cutting. While hard, topaz cleaves easily and should be worn in a mounting that protects the gem from rough treatment.

### The Lure of Opal

After years when opal was out of fashion, this most beautiful of all gems has again found a place in the jeweler's case to display its flashing color and its ever-changing elusive lure. Fine examples, such as the black opal from Lightning Ridge, Australia, now cost as much as $1,000 a carat. As opal is a non-crystalline silica containing a certain amount of water, a stone weighing only a few carats makes an impressive display.

Opal was known and prized in Roman times, and most of the precious opal until about 100 years ago came from what was then Hungary in the form of white opal popular in jewelry. Then the enormously productive Australian fields were discovered, first at White Cliffs and Lightning Ridge in New South Wales, later at Coober Pedy and Andamooka in South Australia.

Some of this opal has historical interest as well as beauty. Fossilized bones and shells, often flashing with opalescence (page 99), as well as opal pseudomorphs of such minerals as glauberite occasionally are turned up by the miner's pick in Australia and Nevada.

Most precious opal has a white or pale yellow body as a background for the sheets or pinpoints of fire that display themselves when the stone is turned (page 76). Black opal has a darker body that accentuates the contrast of colors. Most Mexican opal from near Queretero is what is called fire rather than precious opal, and some is a translucent cherry color that is very attractive in cut stones.

Opal is typically a gem of desert regions, and Virgin Valley in northern Nevada is no exception. Some magnificent specimens of black opal, much of it as replacement of fossil bones, have been mined there, but unfortunately the opal usually dries out and cracks after removal from the rock. This defect makes it undependable for gem use. However, one of the finest opals in existence, the 18.6 ounce Roebling black opal in the Smithsonian Institution, came from there. It has retained its color and integrity for the better part of a century.

Opal lacks the hardness of other silica gems and is also brittle, so that a cut stone should be set in a mounting designed to protect it from abrasion or blows. Abrupt temperature changes such as immersion in hot water when washing the hands, and exposure to grease or oil should also be avoided.

Because opal is often found deposited in paper-thin seams, many gem stones are doublets composed of a thin slice of opal cemented to a backing of some other stone. Often the other stone is black to enhance the fire of the gem by contrast. On such a doublet a dome of transparent quartz may be cemented both for protection of the opal and to magnify its flame. Such triplets are beautiful; they also are more durable and less expensive than a comparable stone of solid opal.

### Garnets

The garnet family comes in many hues—red, green, yellow, brown, orange, violet, purple and colorless—but the most familiar are red garnets. Many families still cherish brooches of deep red Bohemian garnets that belonged to grandmother. These came from what is now Czechoslovakia and were usually mounted in clusters of small faceted stones.

Pyrope, almost ruby red and rarely if ever found as crystals and rarely as large stones, is perhaps the most prized of the red garnets. It occurs as small stones resembling raisins in the sands of northern Arizona near the New Mexico line, and also in Brazil, in the diamond mines of South Africa, and in Russia. Pyrope is sometimes sold as Cape ruby, but is softer and less valuable than real ruby.

Almandine, more plentiful than pyrope and usually darker red in color, has its own outstanding qualities, such as the four-rayed star stones found in Idaho. A form known as rhodolite is a mixture of pyrope and almandine and has its own distinctive amethystine hue. The small rhodolites from North Carolina are especially prized. Rhodolite is also found as larger stones in Africa and Brazil.

Light and lively is an appropriate description of grossular garnet, which is certainly the gayest of the whole family. One of the most attractive forms is called essonite, a distinctive reddish-orange, of which the asbestos mines in Quebec have provided excellent examples. A massive green grossular from Africa is sold under the name of Transvaal jade, which gem it resembles only in color. From the same continent comes the most costly of the garnets, a rare emerald-green grossular that is actually more brilliant than emerald.

Orange of a deeper shade than grossular characterizes gem quality spessartite garnet, found sparsely but in excellent quality in the tourmaline mines of San Diego County, California, and at Amelia Court House, Virginia, as well as in Madagascar and Brazil. Andradite, another garnet, lacks any gem qualities except in an oily green form known as demantoid which has an astonishingly high diamondlike dispersion. The Ural mountains of Siberia and Italy have long supplied demantoid, which often appears in antique jewelry.

Garnets have the requisite hardness for a gem stone but are rather brittle and chip easily.

## The Feldspar Gems

Like the garnets, the feldspars are a family of silicates related in their crystal and chemical structure. The most widely known of the feldspar gems is moonstone, which owes its bluish, silvery sheen to reflections from layers of albite feldspar in orthoclase feldspar. When the stone is cut to a high cabochon, this appears as a shimmering spot of light (see box copy, page 69). Although the commercial gem is usually a milky white, moonstone is found in delicate pink, green, yellow or brown tones, especially among stones from India. Handsome moonstone has come from Amelia Court House, Virginia,

along with green microcline. Another feldspar, peristerite, from Canada, exhibits the moonstone effect against a mottled reddish body color.

The green microline feldspar known as amazonstone or amazonite has gained some following as a gemstone. A handsome dappled variety is found at the Virginia location cited above, as well as in the granite pegmatites of the Pike's Peak region in Colorado. Magnificent groups of this microcline in green or flesh tones with smoky quartz are treasured by mineral collectors.

Sunstone properly is a variety of oligoclase feldspar that sparkles from inclusions, usually of orange-colored hematite or goethite, although the name sunstone is loosely used for other yellow forms of feldspar. The most spectacular feldspar, however, is labradorite, named for the island from which the first and best material was obtained. Properly cut, labradorite flames with broad patches of peacock blue and coppery red and gold like a dusky opal (page 98). Another variety of labradorite is a transparent yellow gem from Utah. Much like it in appearance but available in larger stones is transparent orthoclase from Madagascar. Despite its liveliness and pleasant yellow color, this orthoclase is perhaps too soft and fragile for gemstone use.

## Jade

The name jade has overtones of the mystery we associate with the Orient, but jade is also a thoroughly American stone. Its name comes from the Spanish piedra de ijada, for "stone of the loins" based on the belief it would cure renal colic. Spanish conquistadores brought back many pieces of jade from Central America. Two different minerals are recognized under the name of jade. Nephrite, the jade of ancient China and of the United States, occurs in several colors, usually apple green to dark olive, light gray to black. Under the microscope, nephrite is revealed as composed of matted fibers of the minerals tremolite and actinolite. To this structure nephrite owes its toughness. (Figure 57).

Jadeite, the other jade, was brought by caravans from Burma into China no earlier than the 18th century. Granular rather than felted and a bit harder than nephrite, jadeite revels in color from white through pink and brown to blue, lavender and black, as well as many shades of green, especially the rare and costly translucent "imperial green." California and Guatemala have discovered jadeite, but little of gem quality, while nephrite of good quality is mined in Siberia, New Zealand, Alaska, British Columbia and Wyom-

**57.** Green jade plaque and white (muttonfat) jade bowl from China demonstrate why jade is a favorite carving material. It is tough enough to be carved into thin or intricate outlines without breaking. Central American natives even used it for axes and anvils as well as in jewelry.

ing. Wyoming, however, has passed its prime as a source, except for its splendid black jade.

### Spodumene

Spodumene brings to the gem world the distinctive pink of kunzite and the intense green of hiddenite. The former is named for George F. Kunz, the Tiffany gem expert, and the latter for A. E. Hidden, who helped develop the mines in North Carolina. Chemically spodumene is related to jadeite. Principal sources of transparent kunzite have been in California and Brazil, where some huge crystals have been mined, along with a pale green spodumene.

### Zircon

Zircon has long been popular for its high dispersion, especially in the colorless, blue, yellow and grass-green stones resulting from heating of the reddish-brown pebbles in which the material commonly occurs. Among the natural stones, zircon is diamond's only rival for sparkle. Most of the gem supply comes from Thailand. Zircon is separated from beach sands for industrial use and refined into metallic zirconium.

In a tribute to zircon's diamond-like brilliance, a western jeweler recalls that a rancher, boots,

ten-gallon hat and all, strolled in one day, looked at the cases and picked out a gaudy zircon ring. A few days later he came back and told the jeweler: "I traded that sparkler I bought from you for a team of mules, and now I want another to trade for the wagon and harness."

Colorless zircons are sometimes called Matara diamonds; they are softer than real diamonds and have a higher specific gravity (4.48 to diamond's 3.5). Blue zircons are much heavier than the blue aquamarines for which they are sometimes mistaken (page 80).

### Peridot

A gem popular in Victorian jewelry, the peridot, has returned to favor, partly because a source of large stones was rediscovered not too many years ago. Peridot, or chrysolite, as it is also called, is known to the mineralogist as olivine, a magnesium-iron silicate. In high quality stones, such as those from Burma and the rediscovered source on St. John's island in the Red Sea, the warm green tones are enhanced by the yellow of gold settings. Contrasted with the cool brilliance of emerald, peridot seems warmer and friendlier. Small tumbled stones from Arizona are popular when made up into bracelet bangles or necklaces.

## Lapis Lazuli, Turquoise and Variscite

Lapis lazuli and turquoise have ancient lineage and their own unique place in jewelry. Lapis lazuli, properly a rock, gets its deep violet blue color from the mineral lazurite, its golden glints from inclusions of pyrite, and some of its body from calcite. Pliny likened its color to the "night sky bedecked by stars." In the best grade none of the calcite is made evident by the presence of white spots. Afghanistan has been the major source of fine lapis lazuli for centuries; good to excellent material comes from Chile, Siberia, and Italian mountain near Gunnison, Colorado. "Swiss" or "German" lapis is really dyed chalcedony (see page 78).

Turquoise deposits in several western states make that phosphate of aluminum and copper a typically American gem. Good turquoise is compact enough to take a good polish. Too green a tint is undesirable. American material tends to run somewhat deeper in color than the classic gem from Persia. Both lapis lazuli and turquoise are relatively soft, and a polished gem may become dull from hard use. Turquoise is absorbent, especially in mediocre grades, and should be kept away from grease.

Another phosphate, variscite, found in gem grades in Utah, is popular among amateurs and is even occasionally seen in jewelry stores. Slightly softer than turquoise, it has a distinctively rich green color which may be mottled with gray and yellow.

## Azurite and Malachite

Azurite and malachite, the two hydrous copper carbonates, bring distinctive blues and greens—sometimes mixed together in the same stone—to the jewelry world. Both polish well but are soft and will need repolishing. Masses weighing hundreds of tons were taken from Siberian mines and carved into pillars and table tops for imperial Russian palaces. Magnificent specimens came from the mines at Bisbee, Arizona.

## Pearls

Pearls, coral, amber and jet are alike in several respects; they are gems but not minerals because they are the products of living organisms, and all are associated with the sea. Pearls have been the favored gems of royalty for centuries, Cleopatra of Egypt is reported to have dissolved one in vinegar and drunk it as a beverage, and heaps of them were found in the graves of the North American Mound Builders.

Gem quality pearls come from the shells of a marine oyster and a fresh water mussel, where the pearly material is secreted by the mollusc to coat an irritating particle. Midwestern streams have yielded many pearls from the fresh water mussel genus Quadrula (page 104). Divers and boatmen gather the shellfish, search their flesh for pearls, and sell the shells to button factories. Besides the traditional white and pale pink, pearls are occasionally dark gray, green or rose. Round, teardrop and other symmetrical shapes have the greatest value, but irregular ones, called baroques, have their place in jewelry. Evaluation of pearls is complicated by the number of factors involved: color, the quality known as orient, which is the soft luster, and size. Pearls are graded by these qualities, and then priced by a formula. A grade worth $10 for a one-grain pearl would be worth $40 for a two-grain one and $90 for a three-grain gem. Pearls are soft and porous and are damaged by abrasion, cosmetics and skin acids.

Shells of a number of molluscs are used in decorative jewelry, such as inlays of the iridescent abalone shell, cameos carved from helmet shells, and necklaces made of cowries and a number of other small shells.

## Amber

Amber is a fossil resin, usually some shade of tan or yellow, and cloudy to transparent (page 104). Much of the gem amber was fished from the Baltic Sea, where it washed out of shore deposits and was found floating on the salt water. (The mineral meerschaum used in pipes is found the same way.) Some amber was mined from shore deposits in what is now East Germany. Darker amber comes from Burma, Romania and Sicily. Pieces containing visible fossil insects are highly prized by fossil collectors and amber flecked with bits of bark is occasionally used in jewelry. Most of the beads called amber that come from Africa are copal gum; that from New Zealand is gum from the kauri tree.

## Coral

Coral also comes from the sea, where the tiny members of the colonies take calcium carbonate from the water and build reefs in shallow, warm seas. Little of the living or fossil coral has gem value; pieces of the brilliant red coral large enough for carving are rare; so is a lovely flesh-pink variety teamed in jewelry with black coral. The classic source of gem quality coral has been the Mediterranean Sea, but the pink and black are found in the ocean around Hawaii and off the Mexican gulf coast.

## Jet

Jet, fashionable a century ago for mourning jewelry, has regained some of its popularity through the interest in Victorian styles. The best black jet, a form of lignite, has been collected since Roman times along the Yorkshire coast of England near Whitby. Similar material has come from other places, such as near Las Vegas, New Mexico. Jet polishes well but is not as hard as some of the dyed chalcedony imitations of it.

## Quartz—The Amateur's Delight

Quartz family minerals not only have a place in jewelry stores but they also are the delight of the amateur lapidary. Relatively cheap, abundant, colorful and often patterned attractively, they also occur in places where the amateur can collect them himself.

The family can be divided into two clans, crystalline quartz such as amethyst and rock crystal, and the microscopically-crystalline forms called generally chalcedony, such as agate and carnelian. Colorless quartz, often called rock crystal, is found in huge masses suitable for carving into vases, plaques and similar ornaments. Several locations for collecting large crystals are around Little Rock, Arkansas. When treated with gamma rays, these crystal groups turn a deep smoky color. Natural smoky quartz is not rare; good material is found in Colorado with amazonstone, in North Carolina and elsewhere.

One of the world's meccas for quartz crystal collectors is around Middleville, Herkimer County, N.Y., where the so-called Herkimer "diamonds" occur in cavities in the Little Falls dolomite (Figure 7, page 14). Brilliant and often doubly terminated, these small but perfect crystals can be faceted or used as gems as they are. One man collected them for 50 years and gave his collection of 100,000 crystals, ranging in size from a walnut to a pinhead, to Colgate University. Similar ones are found near Lake George in the same state. Near Roswell, New Mexico, cloudy "Pecos diamonds" are quartz crystals found along the Pecos River. The midwestern Keokuk area where Iowa, Missouri and Illinois are neighbors, has been the source of many splendid geodes lined with quartz crystals.

Yellow quartz (citrine) is popular with amateur faceters because of its beauty and relatively low cost. It is what the jeweler used to sell as topaz and now is known in that trade as quartz topaz. Much citrine is manufactured by heating amethyst or smoky quartz. Rose quartz that is clear enough and deeply colored enough for gem use is rather rare, although some comes from Maine and South Dakota (page 97). Rose quartz that can be cut to display a star is occasionally available.

Amethyst of a rich plum color showing just a hint of red sells by the carat and is the aristocrat among the quartz gems. Like a number of gem stones, such as the corundums, amethyst often has formed in layers of light and dark color, a trait visible if the stone is held to the light and viewed across the length of the crystal. The lapidary must place the bottom part of the cut stone in a zone of the best color to suffuse the cut gem with that color (Figure 55).

The finest American amethyst comes from North and South Carolina. The abundant supply from the Thunder Bay region of Ontario offers only an occasional group of crystals that are not disfigured by a coating of hematite. Mexico in recent years has put on the market delightful groups of amethyst of fair color but excellent crystallization.

Clear quartz containing needles of golden rutile (page 98), black tourmaline or, rarely, some other mineral is often cut to display the inclusions. Tigerseye, a related form, consists of quartz that has replaced fibrous asbestos, keeping the parallel fiber structure which reflects light (page 99). The result is a stone, usually golden-brown, blue or red, which shows bands of dull and bright color as the stone is moved. When cut to a steep cabochon, this will produce the catseye effect known as chatoyancy. Tigerseye when heated turns red, and it can be bleached to a cream color.

In gold mining regions, quartz containing visible gold was often shaped into ring stones, brooches and watch chains. Waterworn nuggets were similarly employed.

Chalcedony embraces a vast variety of such gem minerals as agate, flint, chert, jasper and petrified wood as well as such more established gem materials as chrysoprase, chrysocolla, bloodstone and carnelian. The materials range from translucent to opaque; they are hard and tough and colorful.

Agate is a translucent chalcedony, usually banded or figured—the amateur's favorite stone. Notable varieties are the brown-figured, dendritic moss agate from Montana; nodules of rhyolite with centers of opal and agate, known as thundereggs, from Oregon and California; glacier-worn fortification agates, often described as Lake Superior agates, from Minnesota and the Missis-

**58. Moss agate — an amateur favorite — provides an opportunity to make cabochon jewelry that encloses landscape scenes.**

sippi River gravels; colorful seam agate from Arizona, nodules of a variety of colors from Mexico, and large red-brown nodules from Uruguay and Brazil.

Jasper is opaque but in pattern and color is akin to agate; sometimes the distinction is so difficult to draw that the stone is called jasp-agate. California and Minnesota are among the many sources. Central Ohio supplies the celebrated gem flint of many colors, whose beauty and utility were recognized by the original Americans for their arrow and spear heads. Agatized wood from Arizona, Utah and Texas is popular for jewelry and for such craft projects as book-ends (page 119). From Florida's Hillsborough Bay near Tampa, and from several other places in that state comes another fossil, agatized coral. The geodes are cut open and polished for display (page 102) or broken into pieces and tumbled for craft jewelry.

## Some Notable Quartz Gems

Chrysoprase is one of the few members of the chalcedony family that have a firm place in fine jewelry. Splendid masses from Poland, colored a soft apple green by nickel silicates, were the main source until smaller deposits in Oregon and California were worked. When all these were depleted, chrysoprase of excellent color was found in Queensland, Australia. At its best, this is often mistaken for imperial green jadeite, but it is by no means as expensive.

Chrysocolla, like chrysoprase, is chalcedony stained by another mineral, the soft, earthy hydrous copper silicate chrysocolla, and takes its gem name from that mineral. In good examples it is the color of a summer sky, blue and clean. Gem chrysocolla is often veined with malachite or stained by cuprite or some other copper mineral, which may enhance its value with an attractive pattern or make it worthless. Chrysocolla is found wherever copper is mined, especially in Arizona.

Rich red carnelian and its brown brother, sard, are colored by iron salts. The color is often enhanced by heat treatment, suggested perhaps by the fact that most carnelian comes from hot desert regions. A curious form, called fire agate, is made up of a layer of iridescent red-brown hematite under a layer of clear quartz. It looks like a carnelian opal. Most of it comes from Arizona, New Mexico and Mexico. India and Brazil have long been major sources of carnelian.

Bloodstone, sometimes called heliotrope, is a dense green jasper figured with blood-red spots of iron oxides. Like carnelian, bloodstone has been used for centuries for ring stones, brooches, seals and carvings. A famous example in the National Library in Paris is a statue of the scourging of Christ in which the red appears as blood on his garment. Again India and Brazil are major sources, although good quality bloodstone is found in Georgia, Oregon and Colorado.

## Synthetic Gemstones

Industry has been able to synthesize almost every gemstone. A *synthetic* stone is man made but has the same chemical and crystal character as a rough natural stone. In 1904 August Verneuil began producing ruby, sapphire and the other corundum gems by slowly dusting powdered aluminum oxide and a metallic salt into an oxyhydrogen flame and building up a single crystal on a pedestal. Stones that can be cut to show a six-rayed star are also manufactured, as well as a material like the alexandrite, and a related series of gem materials, the aluminum-magnesium oxide spinels. Gems by the millions are cut from these materials, as well as watch bearings, thread guides in textile mills, and lasers.

Production of synthetic diamonds, a goal of experimenters for a century or more, was achieved in 1955 by the General Electric company. In a heated pressure vessel, diamonds of up to a carat have been made from which gems of ½ carat can be cut, but they are usually too costly to compete as jewelry stones with nature's product. Most synthetic diamond is used as a high quality abrasive in industry.

Natural diamonds have been changed to shades of green or gold by bombardment in a cyclotron. The change in color is only skin deep but is said to be permanent.

Several processes have been developed to give synthetic emerald to the world. Carroll Chatham of San Francisco has grown large stones of excellent quality in a hydrothermal vessel seeded with a natural crystal. The Linde Air Products company, leading manufacturer of synthetic corundum in the United States, and French and German laboratories have also marketed synthetic emeralds. Pierre Gilson of Paris, who has experimented widely in this field, has done the impossible—creating synthetic precious opal as well as turquoise and lapis lazuli.The Gilson turquoise is solid blue with none of the veining of the natural stone. A true chrysoberyl alexandrite synthetic has also come on the market. Like the synthetic emerald, it is cheap only by comparison with the price of a natural stone.

Popularity of the diamond has stimulated production of several synthetics resembling that precious stone. Colorless natural topaz, sapphire and zircon, as well as the high dispersion glass known as strass, have long been used to simulate diamond, but each lacks some essential quality.

**59.  Top, arrangement and names of facets in a brilliant cut gem. Below, other popular cuts of gemstones.**

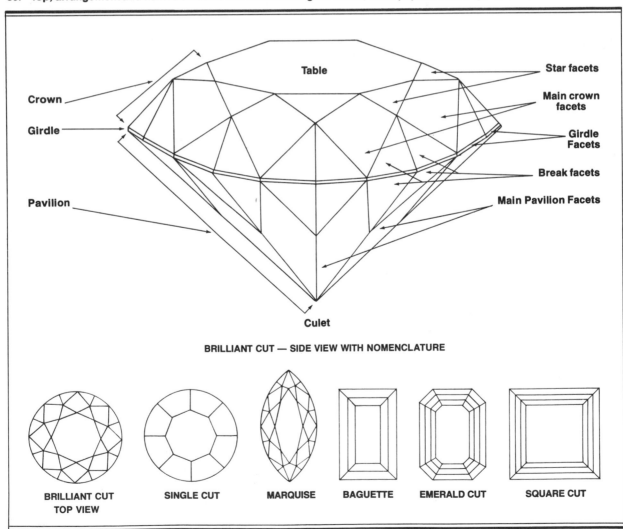

Table

Star facets

Crown

Main crown facets

Girdle

Girdle Facets

Break facets

Main Pavilion Facets

Pavilion

Culet

BRILLIANT CUT — SIDE VIEW WITH NOMENCLATURE

BRILLIANT CUT TOP VIEW    SINGLE CUT    MARQUISE    BAGUETTE    EMERALD CUT    SQUARE CUT

The first synthetic for this purpose appeared on the market in 1948, a pale yellowish rutile that so far outdoes the diamond in dispersion that it gives itself away. Its relative softness and off-color also are objectionable. Somewhat better is strontium titanate, also fairly soft but colorless and closer to the diamond in dispersion, though still more brilliant. This was followed by a much harder synthetic known as YAG, for yttrium aluminum garnet, which has much the appearance of diamond and a hardness of eight on the Mohs scale. YAG can be colored by impurities to imitate other gemstones but its greater brilliance gives it away.

## Imitations And Fakes

Like the Chinese, to whom everything green was jade, ancient peoples mixed glass with genuine stones in their jewelry because they were more interested in appearance than authenticity or value. Many of the stones set in the jewelry and furniture found in the tomb of Egyptian King Tutankhamen are glass. They were used along with genuine stones for ornamental effect. Today glass is used, along with plastics, in costume jewelry, and imitation pearls are glass balls coated with a pearly nacre. Glass feels much warmer than most gemstones and is also softer. It can be scratched by a splinter of quartz or agate but it is harder than moonstone and some other feldspar gems.

Imitations of fine lapis lazuli usually lack the small inclusions of shiny pyrites or the deep blue-violet cast that typifies the finest lapis. If the stone is chipped, the broken surface of real lapis will be dull, that of the dyed chalcedony sold as Swiss or German lapis will be glassy and much harder.

Much natural turquoise is soft or has little color. This is "improved" by dyeing, by rubbing the cut stone with oil, or by crushing poor mate-

### Catseyes, Stars, Chatoyancy and Asterism

Chatoyancy means an effect like the sharp streak of light reflected from a cat's eye. Tiny parallel inclusions in a gemstone reflect the light to the surface. A simple experiment demonstrates the principle as well as that of a related phenomenon, asterism. Sit in your car in the dark facing a bright street light about a city block away. Rub a finger down the side of your nose to pick up a bit of skin oil and make a vertical smear on the windshield. Look through the smear and the light will now appear as a horizontal streak. The tiny parallel lines of oil, in effect a grating, have shaped the light as the fibers do in a gem.

Now make two gentle smears like an X across the first smear and peer through the intersection of the smears. You will see a six-rayed star. This is asterism, the effect that makes a star ruby or sapphire even more precious.

Honey-colored chrysoberyl, although the most costly, is only one of the catseye gems, which include some beryl, quartz, scapolite, spodumene and tourmaline. Star stones can be found in milky and rose quartz as well as the corundums. Garnet, especially that from Idaho, may flash showy stars against the dark red background. Muscovite mica, although not a gem, occasionally contains a dark inclusion in a thin sheet that shows a six-rayed star when the mica is held close to the eye in front of a concentrated light source.

Opal concealed the secret of its inner flames until a few years ago. Then it was discovered that the colors that sweep across a precious opal come from layer on layer of tiny spheres of silica, arranged in orderly rows so that they act much like a diffraction grating. When rays of light strike these layers, part of each ray is reflected back more slowly than the other part; if the grating is such that the slower reflected part interferes with reflection of a nearby ray, it will change the color in that ray. As this happens to a group of rays, the stone will appear colored in the area where the array of spheres is found. Natural opal is made up of patches of such spheres, so different colors appear in patches as the stone is turned in the light. But the color patches in natural opal do not show as pronounced a honeycomb or chicken-wire like texture pattern as do those in synthetic opal (page 80).

Several forms of feldspar, notably moonstone and labradorite, display inner light or color reflections (schiller or adularescence) due to twinning in thin plates or layers that break up and reflect the light, much as the layers of silica spheres do in opal.

Pearls also owe their creamy luster (orient) to thin, semi-translucent layers, like the leaves of a well-formed cabbage, which the oyster built up within its body.

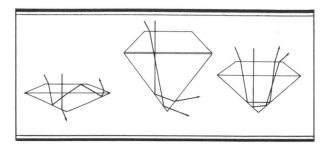

**60.** When the pavilion is too shallow or too deep, light leaks out through the bottom of the stone and much of the brilliance is lost, as explained in Chapter Nine.

rial and molding it in a colored plastic. There is glass turquoise, plastic turquoise, and even imitation spider-web pattern turquoise. The Indian-made marking on a piece of turquoise jewelry is no guarantee; it may have been forged, too. The vogue for Indian jewelry, much of it sold through channels outside the established jewelry trade, has been largely responsible for this undesirable situation.

Amber is imitated with glass, plastics and other resins. One recommended test to distinguish between the real and the imitation is to heat a needle and touch it to an inconspicuous spot on the piece. Amber will give off a pleasant aromatic odor; plastics will give off an astringent odor. Amber feels warmer and lighter than glass.

### Hints on Buying Gems

There are some obvious things to look for in a piece of jewelry or the gems set in it. Begin by sizing it up as you would a person. You would notice his clothing and his grooming. Is the gemstone mounted in a solid gold setting, stamped 10K or higher, of good workmanship? Valuable gems usually appear in appropriate mountings. When examined with a magnifying glass or jeweler's loupe, does the stone appear to be well cut, without showing scratches from the grinding wheel or carelessly-placed facets (Figures 59 and 60)? Some native-cut stones from the Orient are fashioned to get the maximum weight out of the rough material. They are not symmetrical, especially star stones. Such gems may be genuine. Diamonds cut generations ago have a squarish girdle and they are probably of excellent quality.

Most precious stones stand up remarkably well despite long use, although diamonds may show small chips on the girdle. Softer stones should show some signs of wear if they are in an old setting. Hardness of the gem under examination can often be estimated from the kind of polish it

has taken. Most stones passed off as diamonds do not look right to a practiced eye. The zircon often can be identified by looking through the top of the gem for traces of doubling of the bottom facets.

One approach is to try to associate a gem's color with all the gem materials known in that color. Surprisingly enough, if synthetics are ignored, the list is relatively short. The red stones offer good examples. Is this a genuine ruby, or is it a garnet, spinel, or elbaite tourmaline? Large natural rubies are so rare that if a red stone is large, it is probably not a natural ruby. Genuine ruby of high quality has an almost gaudy color when compared with the purplish or dark hue of almandine garnet, the burgundy wine pyrope or the less vigorous tourmaline. Genuine spinel is rarely encountered.

Genuine rubies almost always show some internal defects under a 10-power glass. These are silky patches, small dark masses or angular variations in color (page 79). Synthetic ruby will show swirls of color or bubbles or few if any defects. The same points apply to synthetic sapphire. Among the blue stones few exhibit the brilliance of polish and dramatic depth of color of sapphire. The blue of a heat-treated zircon may be more electric and blue topaz is more likely to be mistaken for aquamarine than sapphire. Blue topaz and high quality aquamarine are strikingly alike and both are valuable.

It usually takes an expert to determine whether an emerald is a natural stone or a synthetic, but he can often identify not only the synthetic but the process by which it was made (page 79). Even the best natural emerald is full of flaws—feathers and inclusions; synthetic emeralds may show a wispy pattern like the smoke trail from a cigarette. More deceptive than synthetics are imitations made by cementing a top of hard stone, such as pale garnet or quartz, on a base of green glass, or a base of material like the top with a thin sheet of green stone or paint between the top and bottom to give the proper color (page 80). The mounting hides the joint. Obviously, no "bargain" stone should ever be bought in a mounting.

Fine quality jadeite cut cabochon closely resembles a slightly cloudy emerald, although the emerald will usually be more translucent and will take a higher polish. Jadeite, too, has been "improved" by heating the polished gem, then plunging it into a green dye which may later fade.

Fine topaz will often have more of a hint of orange or brown in its basic yellow color than citrine quartz for which it is often mistaken. Topaz is also much heavier, and the difference in weight is apparent in stones of the same size.

Star stones are less difficult to judge because the synthetics are so much more showy both in color and in the perfection of the star than all but the most exceptional natural stones. A fine natural chrysoberyl catseye, whether the yellow or green variety, can usually be identified by the sharpness of the eye and the brilliance of the hard gem. Tigerseye and a quartz catseye resemble it, but the former is usually darker in color and the latter is grayish.

With the development of a true synthetic opal, one of the last strongholds of the natural gems has fallen. But there are ways to detect synthetic opals (page 80). It is likely, moreover, that such opals will be fairly costly, but not as costly as fine black opal. Doublet and triplet opals, previously mentioned, are legitimate gems so long as their nature is made clear to the purchaser. Nor has tourmaline escaped; the Gemological Institute of America reports there is now an imitation of bi-colored tourmaline made of quartz.

Gems have value, and where money and value are concerned, especially in this day of synthetics, the buyer must be alert to insure that he gets his money's worth. There are always bargains, but the gem world is a place where a little knowledge is a dangerous thing. The best rule is not to match your wits and knowledge against those of a seller. Buy any gem of considerable worth from a reliable dealer whom you can hold responsible and whom you can trust.

There is another way to look at value, however. If the jewel is attractive and cheap and you like it, buy it and wear it for what it is worth. Probably it is not a bargain, nor an investment, but gems need not be investment; they can be fun, and buying one can be an adventure.

One way to be sure of what you are getting is to do what many collectors do—first find the mineral as described in Chapter Seven, and then shape it into the gemstone you want, as described in Chapter Nine. James L. Kraft, whose enthusiasm for jade never wearied, once wrote: "The collection of rocks and working with minerals is a hobby which can be undertaken with pleasure anywhere in the world, whether a man has a lean or a fat pocketbook. Stones, happily, are everywhere—fascinating, beautiful, mysterious, there for the taking. In every section of the United States there will be found some gemstones, some semi-precious stones of equally great beauty, and a myriad of common everyday stones which have their own satisfactions ...Some states, of course, are richer than others in providing precious stones for the rock explorer. But all of them have some."

# The Colorful World of Minerals

With the pictorial introduction to the vivid world of minerals that begins opposite comes an important caution: Gems and minerals are colored by certain chemicals—usually metal oxides—that are actually impurities. If you could add to beryl minute amounts of chromium—but not enough to change the gem's basic formula—you would have an emerald. That is why there are blue topazes, yellow sapphires, black diamonds, green garnets and red jades. All of these exist in the natural state, and each color is only one of many in which these gems occur.

So the quality we tend to rely on the most—color—is the one that, with few exceptions, can most readily mislead us in identifying gems. In color, garnets and tourmalines can masquerade as emeralds or rubies. Zircons can look like diamonds or aquamarines. Quartz can resemble anything from topaz to jade. And jade can pretend it is a cloudy emerald.

As if that weren't problem enough, synthetic and imitation versions of all precious gems exist, and many are so well made that only an expert can tell the natural from the synthetic or imitation gemstone. On pages 79 and 80 are some clues as to what an expert looks for when he identifies gems and, on pages 113 through 115, some brief insights into other techniques used in identifying minerals. None of these clues will qualify you as an expert gemologist or mineralogist. But they may encourage you to study some of the rich sources of information, listed in Appendix 4, that will increase your knowledge of the subject.

Identifying collectible minerals is easier than identifying gems. As the additional color sections beginning on pages 97 and 113 show, minerals vary in color and appearance, too, but it is often easier to penetrate nature's disguises than man's deceptions. Collectors have many clues to mineral identities, as you will learn in Chapter Three. And once you can identify minerals, you are more than ready to enjoy collecting and displaying them; Chapters Seven and Eight explain how. Or, if you like craftwork, you can begin transforming minerals into useful and beautiful objects, using the techniques described in Chapter Nine. Some appealing projects for beginning craftsmen are shown on pages 119 and 120. Chapter Nine explains how to build them.

**Opposite page.**

C1.   Top of page. This 31-carat Eugenie Blue diamond has perhaps the deepest sapphire blue color of all the famous colored diamonds, which include varying shades of yellow, brown, rose, blue, green and black.

C2.   Center, left. The clear crystal from South Africa shown in a matrix of gray kimberlite is characteristic of uncut gem quality diamonds. While the octahedral shape is common, diamonds occur in other shapes (page 14). Imitations can match the brilliance but nothing equals diamond in hardness.

C3.   Center, right. This faceted 12-carat stone, was cut from the 40.23-carat Uncle Sam diamond, found in 1925 at what is now the Crater of Diamonds State Park in Arkansas.

C4.   Bottom, left. The two emerald crystals in matrix, and the faceted ringstone (inset), have grass green colors characteristic of this form of beryl. Some tourmalines, garnets, and synthetic and imitation emeralds match natural emeralds in color, but they will differ in hardness, brilliance, weight, shape, or the types of flaws in the stone.

C5.   Bottom, right. Beryl crystal from Virgem da Lapa, Brazil, has hexagonal shape and pale green-blue color typical of most beryl. If it were grass green it would be an emerald; if blue, an aquamarine. Golden beryl is called heliodor; pink or pale yellow-orange beryl is morganite; colorless beryl, goshenite. Beryls weigh less than most of the other precious gemstones.

C1

Some familiar
and unusual gems...

C2

C3

C4

C5

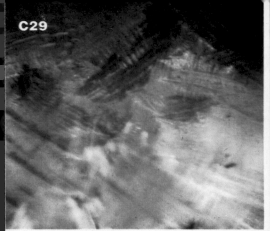

**C29**

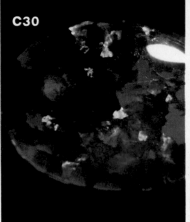

**C30**

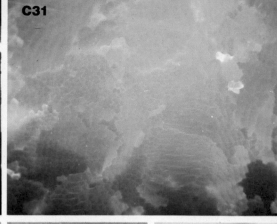

**C31**

**C32**

**C33**

**C34**

**C35**

**C36**

**C37**

C29, C30, C31. **Jades and opals.** Top, left, a devitrified glass called Imori stone is sometimes sold as jade; under magnification it looks like this. Physical tests detect other jade imitations. Top, center and right, synthetic opals display a jigsaw-like structure and, under greater magnification as in the opal at right, a honeycomb or chicken-wire-like texture.

C32, C33, C34, C35, C36. **Zircon, Aquamarine, Topaz, Citrine, and Triplets.** Above, left, the two blue stones—a heat-treated zircon on the left and an aquamarine on the right—are often confused. Zircon's blue may be slightly more electric than aquamarine's, and it is a heavier and less scratch-resistant stone. The yellow cut stones are topaz on the right and its imitator, citrine, on the left. Topaz is heavier and harder than citrine quartz. Far right, viewed from the side, a triplet of spinel shows two pieces joined by a layer of colored cement to enhance the stone's value. Always buy costly gems unmounted so that you can detect doublets and triplets. They are often used with opals, which occur in thin seams, and this practice is legitimate if the buyer is informed of it.

**C38**

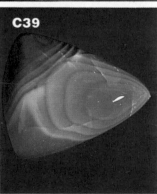

**C39**

# Agate, the amateurs' favorite

C37, C38, C39, C40, C41. No mineral occurs in the infinite variety of colors and patterns that one finds in agates. As a form of quartz, agates are plentiful, durable and they take a fine polish. This makes them a favorite stone with collectors, and with lapidaries who like the challenge of designing jewelry to blend with the agates' colors and patterns. The photographs at left and below are only a small sample of agate's variety. At top is a plume or flower thunderegg agate from Oregon. The polished banded and eye agates, from the Willems collection, are primarily from midwestern locations. (To make the brooch see the information on page 153). The slice of orbicular or eye agate at lower right is from California.

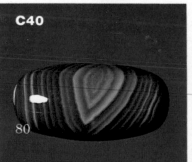

**C40**

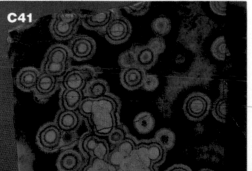

**C41**

80

## Chapter V

# Mother Nature's Exotics

*"True beauty dwells in deep retreats."*
—Wordsworth

The world of flowers has its orchids, the world of animals its giraffes and kangaroos. No less does the mineral world have its own marvels—rocks that bend, rocks made up of threads or needles, rocks formed by lightning, rocks that glow in the dark, and rocks from outer space. All are exotics, a word that the dictionary defines as "striking or unusual in effect or appearance; strange, exciting, glamorous" and of "foreign origin or character." What could be more exotic and foreign than the meteorites and moon rocks that bring us clues to the nature of our universe?

But let us stay with the earthy exotics for a while. Of these, none excites the curiosity or satisfies the sense of beauty more deeply than the phenomenon known as fluorescence. Seeing a dull rock spring into color under an ultraviolet ray lamp is like seeing a Christmas tree lit for the first time. This invisible radiation, the same energy as the rays in sunlight that tan the skin, impresses even those who know nothing about minerals. It is a magic lamp that turns drab rocks into glowing jewels (page 113).

The word fluorescence was coined more than a century ago by Sir G. G. Stokes, an Englishman who observed the effect when he heated a piece of fluorite. Studies since Stokes' time show that the explanation of fluorescence lies in atomic theory and the nature of energy. Minerals, like all substances, are made up of atoms. Each atom is a small world, a densely packed nucleus around which electrons move in orbits like the planets around the sun. When ultraviolet light generated by the lamp hits atoms under favorable circumstances its energy displaces one or more electrons from their orbits. Displacement causes them to absorb energy, which they give back as visible light when they bounce back into place. The color and intensity of that visible light depend on the wave length of the light and the nature of the mineral. If the glow lingers after the source of the ultraviolet light is removed, the mineral is said to phosphoresce.

A precisely-engineered combination of fluorescence and phosphorescence timed so that the fluorescent image remains long enough to be seen but briefly enough to permit the image to move is the principle on which the television picture tube is built.

## Minerals and Fluorescence

A few minerals are always fluorescent and consistent in their color response. Scheelite (calcium tungstate), an ore of tungsten that is used to harden steel, fluoresces a brilliant blue white. Ultraviolet lamps are used to prospect for this mineral and to sort ore in scheelite mines, such as those worked in Idaho and California during World War II.

Despite their use for nuclear energy, few uranium minerals fluoresce. One of them is autunite, which is a micalike calcium and uranium phosphate, that returns a strong yellow green response under the lamp. Some of the world's finest specimens have come from the Daybreak mine near Spokane, Washington.

Calcite is a highly fluorescent mineral, but also highly erratic. At one locality it may react red, at another pink or blue, and with different wave lengths of ultraviolet light the same specimen may change color response. Fluorite, which gave its name to the game, is elusive and reluctant in its response. Sometimes, however, it may show a fluorescent phantom crystal inside an unresponsive one. One resident of Rosiclare, Illinois, a fluorite-mining town on the Ohio River, carved the mineral into sculptures of birds and animals, using fluorescent material to heighten his effects. As an example, a frog that he carved fluoresced on the toes, eyes and tail.

Fluorescence is made possible in most minerals by the presence of some foreign atoms in the right proportions to make the specimen respond. In the Franklin, New Jersey, mines, the willemite which fluoresces green, and the calcite which fluoresces fiery red (page 113), must have a small amount of manganese to activate them. But more than a trace of iron will poison the response.

Ultraviolet is a region in the electromagnetic spectrum of vibrations which range from the

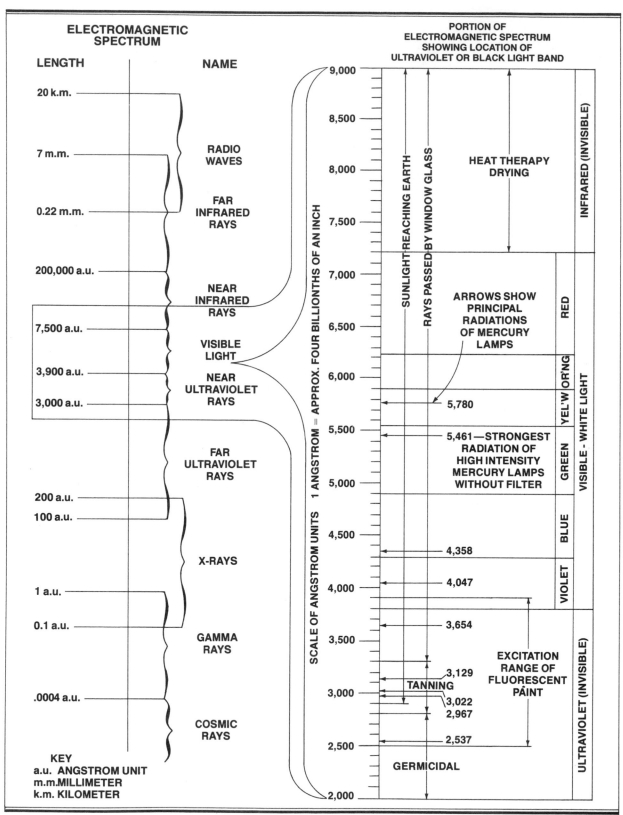

61. In the electromagnetic spectrum, minerals that fluoresce respond to excitation by wave lengths of 2537 (short wave) or 3654 (long wave) ranges, and sometimes to both ranges.

very short, very active cosmic rays and X-rays through the ultraviolet and visible light region to the longer infrared and giant radio waves (Figure 61). Length of the rays, measured from the peak of one wave to the next, is expressed in angstrom units (au.), of which there are nearly 250 million to the inch, or 100 million to a centimeter. Visible light ranges from dark red at 7,000 au. to violet at 4,000 au., while ultraviolet ranges from 4,000 down to about 2,000 au. The faster the particle vibrates, the shorter the wavelength it sends out. In practice, ultraviolet lamps—called black lights—use two groups of rays in the ultraviolet range—long wave around 3,654 au. and short wave at 2,537 au. Part of the sun's light also falls into the ultraviolet range and causes fluorescence but that is masked by visible sunlight.

Some minerals respond only to short wave, others to long, and some to both. Lamps are usually constructed to produce one or the other though both are available in some models. A few minerals that respond to both short and long wave respond with different colors, such as the calcite from Terlingua, Texas. It is blue and phosphorescent under short wave, and pink under the long wave lamp.

The mineral collector uses a hand-held black light lamp resembling a hair brush in size and shape, with a window which passes rays generated by a cold cathode mercury vapor tube. Because ordinary glass screens out the short ultraviolet, the tube is made of fused quartz or a high silica glass. The wavelength that the tube generates is controlled by the pressure within the tube. The window of the lamp is a deep purple to mask off most visible light generated by the tube but to pass the ultraviolet light.

With some minerals, the small amount of visible light passed by the window may be mistaken for a fluorescent response. This can be tested by placing a piece of window glass between the specimen and the tube; the glass will stop ultraviolet light but not visible light. Or the lamp is moved back and forth to see whether the response varies; a true fluorescence response will not change.

## Uses of Fluorescent Light

The zinc mine operators at Franklin and Sterling Hill, in the northern tip of New Jersey, have sorted out high grade willemite ore on the picking tables with short wave lamps. Another use has been found in milling scheelite ore, where the mill tailings are examined under the lamp to ascertain whether scheelite is being lost through poor mill practice. For years the dumps of the Franklin mines have been searched at night by collectors equipped with battery-powered lamps. More than forty fluorescent minerals have come from these mines.

Black light also assists in the search for oil, which shows a characteristic "bloom" or blue-green fluorescence. Drill cores and drill cuttings go under the lamps, and in some areas the ground itself is prospected under ultraviolet lamps for signs of oil brought to the surface by hydrocarbon gases from a buried pool. Oil traces in the crystals cause the fluorite from Clay Center, Ohio, to fluoresce.

## Coals of Fire

Thousands of mine dumps and other rock exposures in North America offer unlimited opportunity to prospect at night with a portable black light outfit. Eyes are more sensitive in the dark, and the fluorescent response more evident. A. L. Flagg, dean of southwestern mineralogists, once estimated that more than 25 fluorescent minerals can be found in Arizona alone. These include agate, chalcedony, calcite, fluorite, hydrozincite, opal, petrified wood, sphalerite, willemite and several uranium minerals. So exciting is Arizona calcite that it was once sold as "coals of fire." Zinc carbonate, the mineral hydrozincite, is another highly fluorescent mineral with a dazzling blue-white response.

## A Telltale Shadow

Cinnabar, the only important ore of mercury, does not fluoresce, but it is always red. Any red-stained rock can be tested for the presence of mercury. A screen is made by dusting fluorescent powder on a cardboard wet with lacquer. The rock is heated in front of the screen so that any mercury will volatilize and cast a shadow when ultraviolet light is projected on the screen; because mercury vapor is opaque to ultraviolet light, the shadow reveals its presence.

Many gems, including some diamonds, fluoresce. With the development of synthetics difficult to distinguish from the natural gems, black light has become one means of testing the source of ruby, emerald, pearls, and other gems. So sensitive are some tests that even the manufacturer of a synthetic can be identified.

Many materials such as sumac wood, plastics, dyes and waxes, petroleum jelly, greases and other substances common to daily life are fluorescent. So are teeth and fingernails. Shirts appear whiter after being laundered because the detergent contains a chemical that leaves the cloth with a slightly bluish fluorescence. In the ultraviolet of sunlight, tattle-tale gray disappears. Flowers with their stems in water containing a fluorescent dye such as fluorescein, rhodamine or eosin will take up the dye and fluoresce in their acquired colors under the lamp.

Fluorescence is also used to detect counterfeit money, the faking or alterations of rare postage stamps, restorations made in old paintings, forged documents, and other situations in which old and new materials may fool the eye but not the light. Black light effects are commonplace in the theater, and even undertakers use fluorescent embalming fluids.

### Fluorescent Mineral Sources

An exhaustive list of locations where fluorescent minerals may be found is impossible because of the unpredictability of response and the vast extent of the United States. Some of the more reliable ones, usually responsive to both waves, unless response to long wave (lw) or short wave (sw) is indicated, are:

**Adamite:** Mapimi, Durango, Mexico, green short wave (sw).

**Agate:** Sweetwater river bed, near Jeffrey City, Wyoming, yellow green from uranium.

**Amber:** Baltic Sea, yellow; not uncommon in any lignite coal exposure.

**Apatite:** Hull, Quebec, yellow.

**Aragonite:** Lovington, New Mexico, red.

**Autunite:** Daybreak Mine, near Spokane, Washington, yellow green.

**Barite:** Palos Verdes, California, cream (also phosphorescent), Elk Creek, South Dakota, brown.

**Benitoite:** San Benito Co., California, blue.

**Brucite:** Wood's Chrome Mine, Texas, Pennsylvania, blue white.

**Bustamite:** Franklin, New Jersey, orange (sw).

**Calcite:** Franklin, New Jersey, red (sw); Picher, Oklahoma, deep green; Deming, New Mexico, yellow green; Bisbee, Arizona, red; Terlingua, Texas, blue (sw), pink (lw).

**Clinohedrite:** Franklin, New Jersey, orange (sw), pink (lw).

**Coral:** Petoskey, Michigan, yellow; Tampa Bay, Florida, cream.

**Diamond:** Blue, often other colors.

**Dolomite:** Bloomington, Indiana, gray green.

**Esperite:** Franklin, New Jersey, yellow (sw).

**Feldspar:** Gillette Quarry, Haddam Neck, Connecticut, albite, orange.

**Fluorite:** Clay Center, Ohio, pale yellow; Rosiclare, Illinois, purple; Weardale, England, blue; Westmoreland, New Hampshire, violet.

**Hackmanite:** Bancroft, Ontario, orange or pink.

**Halite:** Amboy, California, red.

**Hemimorphite:** Goodsprings, Nevada, green (sw).

**Hydrozincite:** Goodsprings, Nevada, blue (sw).

**Manganapatite:** Portland, Connecticut, orange; Franklin, New Jersey, orange (sw).

**Opal:** Baghdad, Arizona, green; San Luis Potosi, Mexico, green; Spruce Pine, North Carolina, (hyalite); brilliant white; Virgin Valley, Nevada, green.

**Petrified Wood:** Eden Valley, Wyoming, green; a number of places in Utah.

**Powellite:** Bishop, California, yellow; Franklin, New Jersey, yellow (sw).

**Ruby (synthetic):** brilliant deep red.

**Scheelite:** Bishop and Atolia, California, blue-white (sw).

**Schroeckingerite:** Wamsutter, Wyoming, yellow-green.

**Septaria:** Utah, orange.

**Tremolite:** Jefferson and St. Lawrence counties, New York, red; Franklin, New Jersey, green (sw).

**Wernerite (scapolite):** Eganville, Ontario, yellow.

**Willemite:** Casa Grande, Arizona; Franklin, New Jersey, green (sw).

**Witherite:** Rosiclare, Illinois, white.

**Wollastonite:** Riverside, California, golden.

**Zircon:** Henderson County, North Carolina; elsewhere in placer mining sands, orange.

Hobbyists fashion fluorescent rocks into spheres, book-ends, jewelry, and table tops that glow in the dark under fluorescent light, and "paint" pictures with grains or chips of selected materials held on the canvas with waterglass. Red-reacting calcite roses and green willemite leaves become a bouquet, and it can be enriched with blue fluorite and yellow wernerite. It is even possible to change the flower arrangement by working out combinations that are one color under short wave and another under long wave. Spring to fall with the flick of the lamp switch.

### The Stones From Heaven

From fluorescent's infinitely small atomic response to the infinitely large universe beyond us is still within the horizons of the mineral world. Celestial visitors—meteorites, tektites and moon and Mars rocks from American exploration of space are exotic in their own right.

The Chinese called meteorites "stones from Heaven." These visitors are the successful ones that complete the trip among the million or so meteors that fall every hour into the earth's atmosphere. The unsuccessful ones burn to dust before they reach the ground or they miss their mark and fly off into space again. All this debris appears to come from disintegrating comets and from the asteroid belt, filled with fragmentary material, that orbits the Sun between Mars and Jupiter. Meteorites appear to represent the primitive material of which the solar system was formed 4.5 billion years ago. For that reason they contain clearer evidence about the origin and nature of the system, and of our earth, than the weathered earth rocks we know.

The arrival of a meteorite is not only important scientifically; it is an awe-inspiring event. Spectators have testified to the cloud trails and blinding glare that mark the approach of such a visitor. Typical is the fall at Amana, Ia., described by Ben Hur Wilson, geologist and teacher at Joliet, Illinois, from contemporary accounts:

> "Between 10 and 11 P.M. on February 12, 1875, as people were going home from gay parties, suddenly the southern sky was filled with bright light from which emerged a ball of fire that lighted the whole earth like lightning. It was accompanied by a rumbling roar like the passing of a heavy train over a trestle bridge, and by several sharp detonations. Horses reared and plunged and dogs howled." The display was visible from Chicago to Omaha and from St. Paul to St. Louis.

Meteorites, especially stony ones, frequently burst with a thunderous roar, falling in a shower of fragments. At Holbrook, Arizona, nearly 16,000 pieces were recovered after a fall there in 1912.

Three general types of meteorites are recognized, iron-nickel, stony and stony-irons. Most of the iron-nickel ones are of a type called octahedrites from their crystal pattern (Figure 62). Most of the ones that are predominantly stone

62. The fingerprint pattern from frictional ablation clearly shows on the surface of this nickel-iron meteorite that fell near Bath Furnace, Kansas.

with some flecks of metal are chondrites because they are filled with small spherical masses of olivine, pyroxene and feldspar called chondrules (Figure 63). The meteorites that are composed almost equally of stone and iron are called pallasites or mesosiderites (Figure 64). Occasionally small diamonds and peridots are found in meteorites.

Octahedrites contain about 8 to 12 per cent nickel; they are coarsely crystallized. Etching brings out the crystal pattern known as Wid-

63. Part of the carbonaceous chondrite that fell near Murchison, Australia, shows fusion crust and claylike interior of this meteorite.

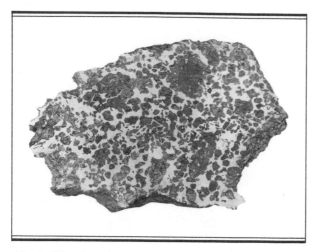

64.   In this stony iron meteorite that fell at Illimaes, Chile, the white areas are olivine, the dark areas, nickel iron.

manstatten figures, named for their discoverer (Figure 9, page 15).

Nine out of ten meteorites are of the stony or stony-iron types, but because the irons are easier to recognize and do not disintegrate as rapidly under weathering, only after systematic search did the predominance of the other types become evident.

Irons, glossy black when freshly fallen, soon grow rusty. They are heavy, magnetic and marked by shallow pits like thumb prints in modeling clay. The pits are caused by air friction

65.   Paragould, Arkansas meteorite that fell in February, 1930 came down in pieces; this chunk weighed 745 pounds.

in the fall, which burns off or ablates the surface of the meteorite so that it often assumes a cone-like shape. Irons range in size from an ounce to one in South Africa estimated to weigh 60 tons.

Stony meteorites are covered with a blackish crust when they arrive, but soon become rusty brown; they are rounded and heavier than the stones likely to be found in a field. Inside they look like gray concrete, often with bits of metal sprinkled through the mass. They are never porous, cindery or layered. One common test is to grind off a corner to look for the telltale glint of metal in the gray stone. Stony meteorites are usually smaller than irons.

### Finding Meteorites

The chance nature of discovering a meteorite, unless it is seen to fall, has made it necessary for scientists to rely on laymen to bring them the material with which they work. Besides contributing to science the lucky one can profit materially. Museums and universities and private collectors compete to get specimens, especially from new falls or ones not represented in their collections.

Ploughs have turned up many specimens. The unusual weight and appearance of a rock from the cotton or corn field often has caused farmers to preserve it as a door stop or a curiosity. Professional collectors make the rounds of rural areas on the trail of such treasures.

Typical of the casualness of most finds is the Sardis meteorite, uncovered by a boy and a mule in a cotton field near Sardis, Georgia, in 1940. The plow fouled on a heavy obstruction. In freeing the plow, the boy uncovered a large flat stone. Suspecting that treasure might be buried under it, he and a friend dug a hole alongside and pushed the stone into the hole. They found no treasure, so the boy covered the stone with earth and went back to plowing. But a few pieces had broken away. The boy noticed that they were heavy and looked like iron. Ultimately the pieces reached the Smithsonian Institution in Washington, D.C., which identified them as having come from a meteorite. Presently, a truck arrived to take the 1,740-pound meteorite to Washington, and the boy got a four-figure check for his discovery.

Another meteorite, known as the Drum Mountain fall, was first seen in 1944 by two Japanese interned in Utah. While prospecting for lapidary material, they ran across a large, dark brown boulder protruding from the ground. Because it was unlike other rocks in that region, they knocked off a small corner with their picks

66.    The meteorite crater at Canyon Diablo near Winslow, Arizona, measures four fifths of a mile across, 570 feet deep.

and sent it to a museum, which later acquired the 1,164-pound specimen.

H. H. Nininger, veteran meteorite hunter, recalls the spectacular fall near Paragould, Arkansas, in 1930. Raymond Parkinson was awakened by the noise and light of the meteorite's arrival, went outside to his pasture field to see whether his horse had been harmed, and found there a fresh hole containing an 85-pound stone which he later sold for $300. Three miles away a 745-pound piece of the same meteorite was discovered (Figure 65). This, the largest meteorite seen to fall up to that time, is now in the Field Museum of Natural History in Chicago. In 1974 a stone weighing 3,894 pounds was seen to fall in Manchuria along with 100 other meteorite fragments.

The most spectacular evidence left in the United State by a meteorite fall is the enormous crater near Winslow, Arizona. Here a great bowl 4,000 feet in diameter, its rim raised 150 to 225 feet above the plain, bears witness to the force with which a gigantic visitor from space struck the earth perhaps 75,000 years ago (Figure 66). Hundreds of pieces of meteoric iron have been

picked up on the surface or have been dug from the soil or the powdered rock within the crater.

The awesome nature of a meteorite fall was glimpsed by some who witnessed the flight of a fireball in August, 1972 near the Wyoming-Idaho-Montana border. Using surveyor's instruments, they calculated its velocity at 10 miles a second, its weight at 1,000 to 4,000 tons, and its energy as that of several atomic bombs. The meteor came within 36 miles of striking the earth before it became lost in space.

Level land surfaces such as deserts, prairies and plateaus are good places to search for meteorites for obvious reasons. They are clear of vegetation and trees, they are dry enough to retard decomposition, and they preserve their markings better than cultivated soil. Plowed fields, rocky uplands and dry lake beds are other promising areas.

Can a meteorite tell us whether life exists elsewhere in the solar system? Perhaps! In 1971 the Field Museum acquired the major part of the Murchison meteorite (Figure 63), a carbonaceous chondrite named for the town north of Melbourne, Australia, where it fell in many pieces in 1969. It is one of only 14 such chondrites among the 2,000 known meteorites, and was especially exciting to scientists because the presence of amino acids was detected in it. Amino acids are the stuff from which proteins, the basis of living matter, are formed. Thus it appears, says Dr. Edward J. Olsen, chairman of the department of geology at the Field Museum, that the initial step from inorganic matter to life is so relatively simple that "life may be vastly more prevalent in the universe than we ever imagined."

Sampling of rarified stratospheric air high above the earth by a high altitude plane revealed that more than half the dust grains there are akin to carbon-rich meteorites and may be fragments of comets. Dustlike meteor fragments also occur in earth-bound dust and sea-floor sediments.

### The Mystery of Tektites

Meteoritics is the science of meteors, and of other puzzling things that come to earth from space. Among these are tektites, small but, as one writer has remarked, "perhaps the most frustrating stones ever found on earth."

Tektites (the name comes from the Greek tektos, meaning molten) are round, button or dumbbell-shaped glassy objects, rarely weighing

**67.** Dark, orange-flecked spheres and fragments are moon soil from the Apollo 17 flight. They contain silicon and iron dioxides, magnesium, calcium, titanium and aluminum oxides and zinc. Scientists are puzzled about what formed them — they aren't related to tektites and don't seem to be formed by volcanic action or meteorite impact.

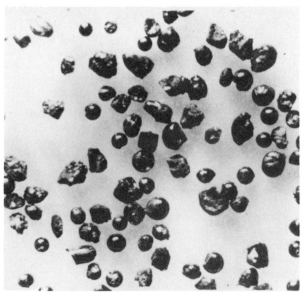

more than an ounce or two. Their surface is pitted and they look dark brown or black but are translucent when held in front of a light. Those of one type, moldavites from Czechoslovakia, are green. Tektites are a natural glass unlike any known earthly material, including the volcanic glass, obsidian.

Most tektites are found in the southwest Pacific area, especially in central Australia, Indonesia and the Philippines. But others come from the Ivory Coast, Africa, Czechoslovakia, and Texas and Georgia. The Texas ones are called bediasites from a town near where they are most common.

For a long time it was argued that tektites came from outer space, possibly the moon, although none has ever been seen to fall. But the newest evidence seems to indicate that tektites are glass splashed out as molten drops where giant meteorites struck the earth.

Like the sacred stone of Kaaba, at Mecca in Arabia, which is worshiped by the Moslems and is probably a meteorite, tektites have for centuries been regarded as talismans of great power in the Orient. Polynesian rulers believed that these stones would bring them wealth and many children. They called them by the name Agni Mani, which is interpreted as the Sanskrit for fire gem.

### Moon and Mars Rocks

In the sense of being foreign, no more exotic rocks exist than those on the moon and Mars our scientists have been studying. Yet in many ways they are hauntingly familiar. All moon rocks are igneous—formed by the cooling of molten magma. The dark moon regions—called maria—that form the features of the "man in the Moon" are basaltic lavas similar to the lavas that come from Hawaiian volcanoes. The light regions—called highlands—are once-molten rocks that cooled slowly deep within the moon, and are closely enough related to earth rocks formed the same way to be called gabbro, norite and anorthosite—all of which are familiar earth rocks. Moon rocks do contain the same elements as earth rocks but the amounts of the elements in each may differ. Some familiar minerals in moon rocks are plagioclase feldspar, ilmenite, pyroxene, olivine and cristobalite (see page 114, and Figure 67).

Much aluminum and calcium is found in the highland rocks, less in the dark maria rocks which contain more iron, titanium and magnesium. While all earth rocks contain detectable amounts of water, no moon rocks do. Since they could not react with water to form clays, shales or limestones, moon rocks 3.5 billion years old look younger and fresher than water-bearing lava recently erupted from a volcano on earth. There is almost no free oxygen on the airless moon, making it possible for moon rocks to contain small amounts of metallic iron. They also contain tiny amounts of the carbon compounds from which life is built, but most of the carbon came to the moon in meteorites and solar winds. This, plus the absence of water, explains why no signs of life or fossils are found on the sterile moon.

Like the earth, the moon has a crust and a mantle but we are not yet sure that it has a molten iron core like earth's. Some heat comes from within the moon but it is less than scientists had anticipated. The moon's last volcanic eruptions occurred several billion years ago. Since then, only bombardment from large meteorites and particles from solar winds have altered the moon's surface, which has changed little. By way of contrast, the restless earth with its volcanoes, earthquakes and ceaseless mountain building and destroying puts on a new face (and, in the process, creates new rocks) every day.

Martian geology is in some ways more like earth's than the moon's. Mars surface shows signs of much water and wind erosion as well as volcanic activity, and far fewer craters than the moon. Rock samples analysed by the Viking Lander appear to be basalts containing mixtures of hydrated minerals. In addition to a high iron content, they contain significant amounts of calcium, silicon, sulphur and aluminum (though not as much aluminum as is found in earth's

basaltic rocks). Minor quantities of titanium are also present. Five to ten percent of the surface material on Mars is magnetic and significant amounts of magnetite may be present. The fine layer of dust that covered all of the rocks that have been sampled to date is colored red by ferric oxides.

Although no complex organic compounds were found in the first Martian samples, the presence of carbon, water, oxygen, carbon dioxide and other chemicals associated with living organisms will lead to additional research to determine whether such organisms could—or at one time did—live on that planet.

## Rocks Formed by Lightning

A more homely but still impressive example of the power of nature exists in the oddity called a fulgerite. When lightning strikes in loose sand such as the dunes at the south end of Lake Michigan or at Nags Head, North Carolina, it fuses silica grains into a long, hollow pipe of glass (Figure 68). This is a fulgerite. They are fairly rare in collections, partly because they are difficult to find and more difficult to remove in one piece. A specimen may be only a few inches long or, in exceptional circumstances, as much as 10 feet long, and it may branch into fantastic patterns.

## Some "Soft" Rocks

A number of minerals defy the conventional notion that such things are "hard as a rock." Asbestos is a solid mass, but it can be turned into silken threads and woven into cloth (Figure 1, page 11). Because it is fire and acidproof, asbestos possesses the qualities called for in brake linings, fire-fighters' garments and theater curtains. Short fibers are manufactured into fireproof shingles and insulating materials. Large mines in Quebec supply much of the world's asbestos.

Both tremolite and actinolite, two members of the amphibole family closely related to nephrite jade, are found in fibrous form and are suitable for some industrial purposes. They have a quirk all their own called mountain leather, a natural asbestos-like sheet of tough interlaced fibers so light it will float. One collector ran across what he took to be a pile of old paper sacks on a mountain slope. On closer scrutiny he saw that they were huge sheets of mountain leather as large as 3 by 5 feet square. Too uncommon to have any commercial use, mountain leather is prized by collectors.

**68. Lightning formed this slender tube of fused sand which is called a fulgerite.**

## Rocks that Bend

Some rocks bend. Mica is one. Another is itacolumite, better known as flexible sandstone. This is a light-colored, porous rock made up of interlocked grains of sand held together by scales of mica. As a strip of this rock is bent gingerly, the grains rotate on adjoining grains without separating. Itacolumite comes from Georgia and North Carolina as well as the diamond-mining regions of Brazil and the Ural mountains in Russia. *Rocks and Minerals* magazine once published a picture of a circle 210 inches in circumference made up of ten 21-inch strips of this flexible sandstone. Each strip was bent 3 inches.

Minerals often pick up foreign matter as they crystallize, but few examples exceed in interest the sand calcites from Rattlesnake Butte in South Dakota. Here calcium carbonate solutions cemented the glistening beige sand into the shape of calcite crystals, forming random groupings of doubly-terminated hexagons that are dramatic additions to any collection (Figure 69). In size the crystals range from less than an inch to great groups beyond the strength of one man to lift.

## Rocks that Wriggle

Perhaps you or your father or grandfather can remember when every child had fireworks of his own on July 4th. One of the most harmless among them turned into wriggling worms when

**69. Group of sand calcite crystals is from South Dakota.**

touched with a match. This was based on the odd property of a mineral called vermiculite, a light yellow to brown altered mica, which swells as it loses water under the influence of heat and expands into wormlike threads that occupy six times the bulk of the original material. Today industry uses vermiculite and perlite, a volcanic glass, to make light-weight plaster and concrete.

Equally curious is the habit of black manganese oxides that push their way into other rocks in the guise of branching, mossy, fernlike growths so lifelike that they are often mistaken for fossils. To these growths Montana moss agate owes the curious patterns that endear it to the lapidary (Figure 6, page 13). They also appear in the fluorescent Sweetwater moss agate and in some common opal. Their full glory, however, is to be observed in bedding planes of white limestone.

Modern man is not the only one who was attracted by these dendritic habits of the manganese minerals. In his book on magic, *The Golden Bough,* Sir James Frazier writes:

"The ancients set great store on the magical qualities of precious stones. Indeed, it has been maintained with great show of reason that such stones were used as amulets long before they were worn as mere ornaments. Thus the Greeks gave the name of Tree Agate to a stone which exhibits tree-like markings, and they thought that if two of these gems were tied to the horns and necks of oxen at the plough, the crops would be plentiful."

Gold, silver and copper, all of which belong to the isometric system, crystallize in dendritic forms made up of twinned, flattened cubes that look like triangular pyramids. Cuprite, which belongs to the same mineral system, however, builds its most exotic form, chalcotrichite, into brilliant red hairs made up of cubes piled on end. Unlike these crystalline curiosities, the manganese dendrites are colloidal in nature.

A touching story is told about fairy crosses, one of the twin forms in which the mineral staurolite occurs. In Patrick County, Virginia, one of the best places to find these exotic crystals, they say the fairies were dancing around a spring when an elf brought word of the crucifixion of Christ. The fairies burst into tears at the sad news and their tears became fairy crosses. In this same region, people cherish the tradition that Pocahontas, daughter of the Chief Powhatan who ruled this region, wore a necklace of fairy crosses. She gave one to her English friend, Capt. John Smith, as a talisman against harm.

Equally curious but rarer are the crystals of andalusite in which white, cross-shaped patterns

70. Chiastolite is a form of andalusite in which white inclusions form a cross-shaped pattern against background of black carbon.

appear throughout the crystal against a black background of carbon inclusions. From this habit the mineral variety is called chiastolite, (Greek for cross-stone). A series of slices through such a crystal reveals a fascinating progression toward the nearly perfect cross.

## Exotic Mineral Inclusions

Porphyry, as has been explained in Chapter 2, is a type of igneous rock in which large crystals formed before the magma was suddenly chilled into a fine-grained ground mass. They stand out from the mass like water lilies in a pond or raisins in a slice of bread. Some of these are among

the real exotics of the mineral world. A list of striking examples would include the chrysanthemum stones that Japanese cherish, similar beauties from Vancouver Island in Canada, and handsomely-figured porphyries from the Lake Superior region. In all of these the lath-like crystals of feldspar are grouped into patterns that look like petals against the black basalt background. They make superb book-ends or decorative groupings around plants.

Some crystals are hospitable to foreign matter. Quartz, an open-door host, may be colored green by fine particles of a chlorite mineral, red by flecks of hematite or may set up a splendid background for arrows of black tourmaline or golden sheaves of rutile needles which were once called Venus hairs or arrows of love (page 98). Quartz crystals even disfigure themselves with inclusions of mud or with waterfilled cavities in which a bubble can be seen to move as the crystal is tilted.

Imaginative collectors amuse themselves by searching for faces and meaningful forms in agates and other lapidary materials. The late J.L. Kraft was fond of showing an agate containing a pattern not unlike the profile of President Franklin D. Roosevelt with cigaret holder at a jaunty angle. Some others are shown in Figure 71.

Nature hides some of her noblest creations inside geodes, nodules and concretions. Having the opportunity of opening these, of being the first person to discover what is inside, is an exciting experience. A geode is defined as an enclosed shell, usually of quartz or calcite, filled with crystals projecting into the hollow interior. It is separated from its limestone matrix by a film of clay. The celebrated geodes of the Illinois-Iowa-Missouri area that take their name from Keokuk, Iowa, conform admirably to this description. Some appear to fill a space left by the

71. Left, can you find the praying hands, fox head, or bird in a nest? Or perhaps you would prefer the calcite poodle at right? Looking for such exotic patterns is a favorite pastime with collectors.

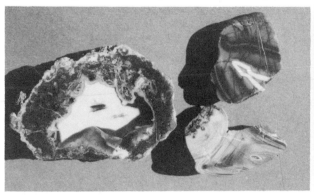

72.   **Some typical forms of sedimentary concretions.**

73.   **Stalactite descending from ceiling is about to join stalagmite growing from floor to form a pillar. Note in background that a dripstone waterfall is about to form; many cave walls are built of such formations.**

decay of a swollen organism. When the saw or hammer opens a geode a whole array of crystals of quartz, calcite, barite, hematite, millerite and ankerite may appear, sometimes blackened by crude oil. Geodes from other areas, notably Chihuahua, Mexico, and Brazil and Uruguay, contain amethyst crystals.

A nodule differs from a geode. It is a small, rounded, solid body, usually harder than the rock in which it has formed. A concretion can be regarded as a special kind of nodule, formed of particles of like composition that have grown together, such as pyrite balls and clay-ironstone nodules. The lapidary-minded collector especially prizes the nodules from the lava plateaus of the northwestern United States that he calls thundereggs. These have formed in gas cavities in the reddish rhyolite. Inside they display blue agate, pinkish opal and the lovely flowerlike patterns for which these nodules are famous.

Concretions arouse the curiosity of many rockhounds because they can simulate Eskimo sculptures (Figure 17, page 19), fossils and a number of other things that they are not. Concretions are usually light gray, somewhat harder than the sedimentary rocks in which they occur, and have softly rounded contours (Figure 72).

Many fossils of the coal-forming ages millions of years ago are preserved in concretions, red or gray on the outside, which open up to show a fern leaf, a piece of bark, or a shrimp preserved as a fossil tracery. In a few areas, so-called Indian rattle boxes, a natural toy for the subjunior rockhound, are occasionally to be picked up. When shaken these give a swishing or rattling sound from sand or gravel inside.

### The World of Caves

Nowhere does the mineral world appear more unwordly than in a cave. Here nature has worked its wonders with the simplest of means and tools. Water trickling through the soil above a limestone deposit carries with it a mild acid formed from the air's carbon dioxide. Moving through joints in the rock, the acid dissolves the

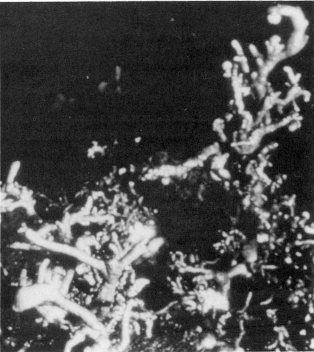

74. Left, a cave formation of feathery aragonite crystals. Right, mysterious helectite formations in Wyandotte Caves, Indiana, that grow out in gravity-defying branches.

stone and, because nature has time on her side, at last creates a cave. As the carbonate-laden waters continue to drip into the cave, a hollow tube of calcite or aragonite shaped like a soda straw grows from the ceiling. Slowly the tube swells and becomes a stalactite. Some of the moisture drops to the floor of the cave and builds up a pillar of stone rising toward the stalactite. Remember the word stalactite has a "c" in it for ceiling; stalagmite has a "g" in it for ground. If the two meet, a pillar is the result (Figure 73).

Water seeping through a crack will form a drapery or curtain, pleated or ruffled like a cloth curtain, or it may take on the likeness of a waterfall. These formations are called dripstone. Caves vary widely in their wonders, which may include bone-white formations celebrated for their majesty, delicacy or ghostly impact (Figure 74), caves in which metallic salts such as iron oxides have tinted the formations with colors beautiful in the flickering light of candles, or caves where the size and massiveness of the fancifully-named masses awe the beholder.

One curious formation develops where dripping water collects in a pool on the floor. Under the right conditions it may roll bits of rock around in the pool so that they become coated with calcite. Cave pearls are the result; they look like albino eggs in a bird's nest (Figure 75).

Caves are wonderlands and should be left that way. They are not places to collect but places where cave explorers can satisfy their craving for adventure and the rest of us can visit and continue to enjoy.

Other forms of exotic minerals that can be collected are the fossils, those mysterious ghosts of the living from ages past that intrigue so many collectors. We shall learn more about them in the following chapter.

75. Cave pearls formed when bits of rock are rolled around in a cave pool and covered with calcite.

## Chapter VI

# History Underfoot

*"Look into the seeds of time."*
　　　　　　　—Shakespeare

Fishing for sharks in the hills of Montana may sound like a waste of time. But scientists recently found fossils from what seems to have been a golden age of sharks at Bear Gulch, southeast of Lewiston, Montana, and 6,000 feet above sea level. The soft limestone deposited there by an ancient sea 320 million years ago preserved an astonishing variety of sharks. Some were shaped like flounders, some had enlarged fins like flying fish, some had a spike and others crablike claws on their snouts, and one 4-foot long shark had a dorsal fin hinged like a rudder. One variety was only 1¼-inch long. In the same limestone were found shrimp, worms, and five varieties of coelacanth, a 450-million year old species of fish that was thought to be extinct until a live one was found in 1938.

Scientists also found the shark fishing good in a creek north of Terre Haute, Indiana, where the remains of 2,000 sharks and other marine animals have been dug from the creek bed shale. Compared to the Montana sharks, the Indiana sharks were relative newcomers, having died and been preserved some 250 million years ago.

Millions of years after the Indiana sharks perished, the sticky tar of the Rancho la Brea pits in what is now Los Angeles trapped browsing animals and the predators who came to eat them. Sloths, mastodons, mammoths, the sabertooth cat Smilodon, bears, and many smaller animals and even insects have been taken from the vast bone beds in the pits. Some 1,500 skulls of Smilodon—a cat larger than today's tiger with 8-inch long canine teeth—have been recovered.

In Paluxy Creek, near Glen Rose, Texas, tracks record a life-and-death race between a vegetarian dinosaur that was being pursued by a carnivorous one. From the tracks paleontologists have drawn conclusions about the body structure and wading habits of some species of these giant creatures. Dinosaur tracks are not uncommon. They have also been found in the Connecticut valley, New Jersey, Colorado, and in Dorset, England, and a number of other places in the world.

76. **Life was a bit crowded when this form of trilobite, Homotelus bromidensis Esker, covered the sea floor 600 million years ago at what is now Bromide Crossing in the Arbuckle mountains of Oklahoma.**

## Fascination of Fossils

These four glimpses into the life of the past explain something of the dramatic fascination that fossils possess. They introduce us to beings that, like ourselves, enjoyed the warmth of life. From them we can begin to sense our own primeval roots, and learn about the diversity of other creatures—plants and animals—who preceded us here.

That may be one reason children enjoy hunting for fossils so much. When a Chicago newspaper described one family's hunt for fern fossils in the strip mines of nearby Will County, the dumps were thronged for weeks thereafter with families whose eager children couldn't wait to go fossil hunting.

## What a Fossil is

A fossil is any preserved evidence of life in the geologic past. Most fossils are at least several hundred years old. They may be as huge as the bones of giant dinosaurs (Figure 78), or as microscopic as algae. They may be a bone, a shell, the impression left by a plant leaf, an animal

77.   What life at sea was like in the early Ordovician epoch. Note crinoids waving over the corals at left, several forms of trilobites in right foreground, and the white mollusc about to lunch on a butterfly shaped brachiopod.

track, a worm burrow, or even coal and oil. Paleontology is the study of fossils.

Most fossils are organic matter that has turned to stone, but there are exceptions. At one extreme is the body of a mammoth found in Siberia or Alaska, frozen so rapidly by some catastrophe that its mouth is still filled with the grass it was munching when it perished. Eskimos have thawed mammoths and fed the flesh to their dogs. Shells and shark teeth, even bones preserved over millions of years in the phosphate deposits of Florida, retain their original shape and substance (Figure 79 and 80).

Far commoner, however, are fossils in which some or all of the organism has been replaced by a mineral, such as quartz, calcite, opal or pyrite (see page 101). The mineral may merely infiltrate the empty cell spaces in wood or bone, so that much of the original organic material remains and retains its cell structure. Or it may go a step farther and replace, molecule by molecule, the organic material so that nothing of the latter

remains except its appearance. Most petrified wood is formed in either of these ways (Figure 81). So are the eagerly sought Petoskey stones of fossilized coral from northern Michigan (Figure 82), and the Utah horn corals turned into brilliant red chalcedony.

Remarkable detail of the original plant tissue is preserved as carbon films in shale and in clay-ironstone concretions from strip coal mines such as those south of Chicago in Will and Grundy counties, and in parts of Pennsylvania and elsewhere. Besides the fern and bark species, scores of insects, shrimp, worms and other animals appear in these fossil cemeteries. Volcanic ash and mud flows created an ideal environment for plant and insect fossils near Florissant, Colorado, and for fish skeletons in the Green River shales of Wyoming (Figure 83). Near Barstow, California, insects in startling detail can be found in nodules in the desert hills.

Nature creates many fossils by a method similar to that used by the sculptor who works in

**78.** An early dinosaur find was this 675-pound femur (upper hind leg bone) of a brachiosaurus, one of the biggest of all dinosaurs. Recent research in wind tunnels and elsewhere suggests dinosaurs were not the plodding, cold-blooded giants of movie fiction. At least they had enough sense to evolve into the birds we have today.

**79.** Like their owners, shark's teeth have come in all sizes ever since their first ancestors appeared about 500 million years ago. These, from Florida and New Jersey, are Genus Carcharodon (the large ones) and Genus Odontaspia (the slender curved ones).

Plaster casts from these molds depict the citizens of the doomed city in all the agony of their futile attempts to escape.

## Conditions for Fossilization

In the billions of years that our earth has existed, an unimaginable number of plants and animals lived, flourished and died. Relatively few became fossils, for only by a series of fortunate accidents does an organism leave its obituary written in stone. Organic matter will decay quickly, unless the decay is prevented by some circumstance. Freezing saved the flesh of the mammoths, poisonous waters or layers of mud may forestall scavengers and destructive exposure to the air, as in the case of the Indiana sharks. Mineral-rich solutions and the deposition of sedimentary rock can then get to work and complete the fossilizing process.

Fossils are not actually rare. Nearly every state in the United States has its characteristic types, and some are plentiful. Like other Midwestern states as far down as Texas, Ohio has an abundance of fossils in exposed limestones and shales. Big Bone Lick in Kentucky is a famous locality. Here ancient sloths and bisons came to the salt lick near where Big Bone Creek empties into the Ohio River. Thomas Jefferson had bones collected here for the White House.

Some rock formations don't have much to offer the amateur paleontologist. Hot igneous rocks, especially lavas, cannot be expected to preserve even traces of once-living things, except as chalcedony-filled casts of trees or in such excep-

clay, then makes a plaster mold of his statue and casts it in bronze. An organism embedded after death in mud or ooze may decay, leaving a space in its own image in the hardening sediments. If this natural mold fills with a mineral such as calcite, quartz, hematite or pyrite, a duplicate of the shape of the plant or animal will be the result. The insects preserved in amber from the Baltic Sea are actually minutely-detailed carbon film replicas of the insect in the gum from an ancient tree (page 104). Casts of shells formed of translucent quartz are found in Hillsborough Bay, off Tampa, Florida. Perhaps the most celebrated examples are the molds formed of human bodies when lava and ashes from the volcano Vesuvius poured on the Roman city of Pompeii.

**C42**

**C42, C43.** Left. Crystals of kunzite, are a pink form of spodumene. Below. Crystals of rose quartz are rarely found in transparent, gem-quality specimens. Rose quartz crystals are hexagonal; spodumene's are monoclinic and the mineral is somewhat heavier than quartz.

**C43**

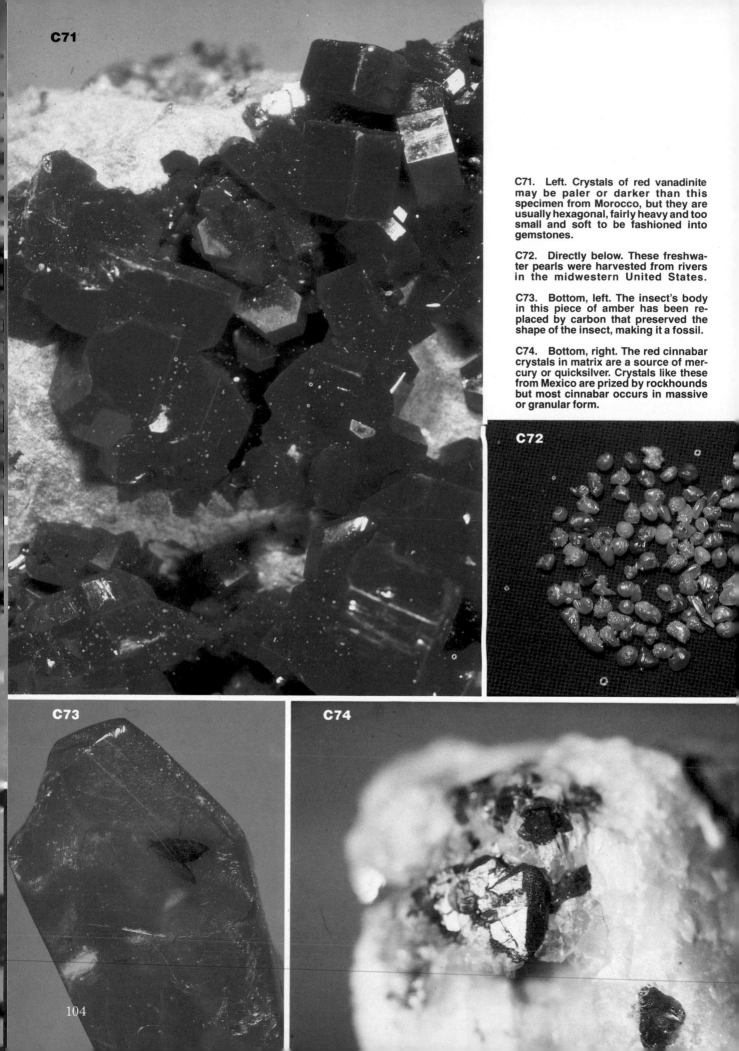

**C71.** Left. Crystals of red vanadinite may be paler or darker than this specimen from Morocco, but they are usually hexagonal, fairly heavy and too small and soft to be fashioned into gemstones.

**C72.** Directly below. These freshwater pearls were harvested from rivers in the midwestern United States.

**C73.** Bottom, left. The insect's body in this piece of amber has been replaced by carbon that preserved the shape of the insect, making it a fossil.

**C74.** Bottom, right. The red cinnabar crystals in matrix are a source of mercury or quicksilver. Crystals like these from Mexico are prized by rockhounds but most cinnabar occurs in massive or granular form.

80. Man cannot match nature's ability to make exact replicas of living originals, as these fossil shells from Florida show. They are Genus Vasum (top), Melongena (left) and Cancellaria (right).

82. Petoskey stone is a fossilized Hexagonaria coral from Michigan that takes a fine polish.

tional conditions as existed at Pompeii, where vapors and gases killed the people whose bodies were then buried in volcanic ejecta. The schists, quartzites and other metamorphic rocks rarely retain recognizable traces of the fossils they may once have held. But the seas that laid down shales and limestones in the midcontinent brought with them bony fishes, shrimp, jellyfish among a multitude of other creatures, and gave them decent burial in sedimentary rocks.

In Colorado, Wyoming, Utah and Arizona the sandstones and limestones that later seas and winds created—the strata of the Grand Canyon—preserve the bones of dinosaurs and other creatures born too late to appear in Midwestern rocks.

81. Ancient trees rivaled dinosaurs in size, as these agatized logs from the Petrified Forest National Park show.

## The Dimension of Time

To hold in one's hand a fossil 500 million years old, incomprehensible as that figure is, is impressive. But when we are told that the fossil is just a youngster in a universe that is billions of years old, the mind becomes numb, just as it does when we hear of multi-billion dollar deficits. For an analogy that will help us comprehend where that fossil and mankind belong in time, imagine earth's long history reduced to the length of one year. January through June would be lifeless, so far as the record in the rocks indicates. In July and August we would begin to find traces of one-celled and other primitive life. Mammals would not appear until about December 10 and man not until 11:45 p.m. on December 31. Of that last 15 minutes history records only the last 60 seconds. Man and civilization are rank newcomers indeed.

Most of what is known about the earth's past has come from a systematic study of fossils and the sedimentary rocks in which they are found. Less than 200 years ago, it was widely believed that the earth was little more than 4,000 years old. Then man discovered that the rocks and their fossils were the real keys to geological history. From these, it was possible to build the geological time scale shown in Table D.

From this record, it is obvious that at least half of geological time tells us little about the past. But life must have existed, for the organisms in Paleozoic (Ancient Life) rocks are so advanced that they had a long history of evolution behind them. In Cambrian seas, worms

105

## TABLE D

| ERA | PERIOD | EPOCH | MAJOR EVENTS | YEARS IN PAST |
|---|---|---|---|---|
| CENOZOIC | Quaternary | Recent | Historic man | 11,000 |
| | | Pleistocene | Glaciers, primitive man | 3 million |
| | | | Mammals at peak | 13 million |
| | Tertiary | Pliocene | Mastodons widespread | 25 million |
| | | Miocene | Modern mammals, plants | 36 million |
| | | Oligocene | First horses, whales | 58 million |
| | | Eocene | Mammals dominant on | 63 million |
| | | Paleocene | land; modern birds | |
| MESOZOIC | Cretaceous | | Flowering plants, extinction of the dinosaurs and the ammonites | 135 million |
| | Jurassic | | Giant dinosaurs, ammonites. First birds and rise of mammals | 180 million |
| | Triassic | | First dinosaurs; cycads and conifers flourish. | 230 million |
| PALEOZOIC | Permian | | Mammal-like reptiles. Trilobites and many marine animals vanish. | 280 million |
| | Pennsylvanian | | Coal laid down in swamps; first reptiles Amphibians abundant. | 310 million |
| | Mississippian | | Rise of scale trees and tree ferns. | 345 million |
| | Devonian | | First amphibians; age of fishes Eurypterids at peak. | 405 million |
| | Silurian | | Plants take over land | 425 million |
| | Ordovician | | First fishes; great development of sea life, corals and cephalopods. | 500 million |
| | Cambrian | | Trilobites and brachiopods rule as sea life appears in fossil record. | 600 million |
| PRECAMBRIAN | Proterozoic | | Fossils rude and rare. Bacteria, fungi emerge | |
| | Archeozoic | | Oldest algae, most ancient rocks | 4.5 billion |

(For the collector who wishes to remember the periods of the Paleozoic Era in order, try this sentence: "Coeds On Saturday Dates Must Primp Pretty." (Cambrian, Ordovician, Silurian, Devonian, Mississippian, Pennsylvanian and Permian.)

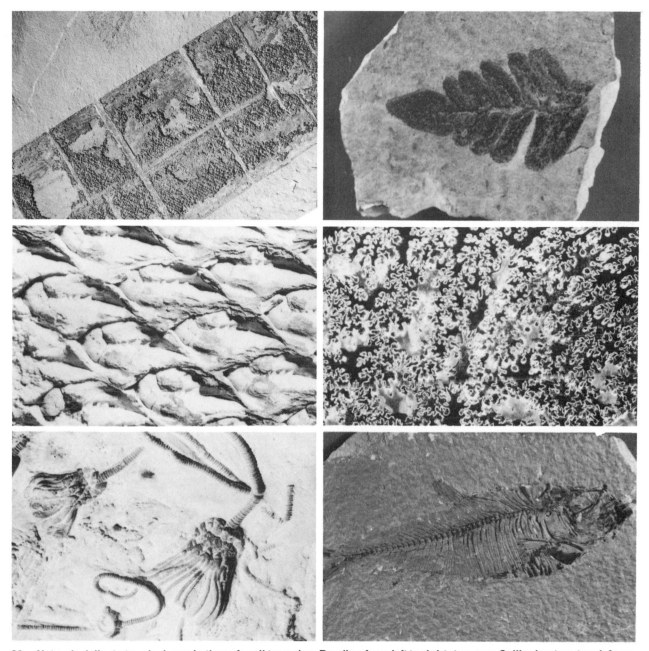

83. Nature's delicate touch shows in these fossil traceries. Reading from left to right: top row, **Callixylon** tree trunk from **Michigan**, and **Neuropteris** leaf from **Iowa**; second row, **Lepidodendron** bark and **Ammonite** shell pattern from **South Dakota**; third row, **crinoids** from LeGrand, Iowa and **Genus Diplomatus** fossil fish from Wyoming.

wriggled through the masses of sponges; shelled brachiopods and armored trilobites ruled the sea bottoms, and plants were developing beyond the algae stage. By the Mesozoic (Middle Life) era, dinosaurs were the lords of the earth, while the first birds and mammals pointed the way evolution would go. We live in the Cenozoic (Recent Life) era which has given us the plants and animals that make life possible for man.

Fossils from rocks formed in these eras are the bookmarks of evolution. The Chinese with their genius for appropriate imagery have called stratified rocks "the book of 10,000 volumes." But in this book, unlike our history books, the order of the pages is reversed. What geologists call the law of superposition states that normally the rocks appear in order of age with the oldest at the bottom and the youngest at the top.

It was an English canal engineer named William Smith who two centuries ago noticed that his excavations cut through strata of limestone that contained the same sequence of fossils, especially ammonites. By this sequence he could recognize the similarity of the strata at various sites and could correlate their order. Like strata contained like fossils; the fossils fingerprinted them. From this discovery it became possible to trace rock formations across wide areas, make geological maps, assign the rocks to an orderly sequence in time, and plot the progressive changes in fossil organisms. Only the voice of a Darwin was then needed to transform such information into the theory of evolution on which several major sciences are based.

In the United States, the Silica shale and the Columbus limestone of the fossil-rich quarry at Silica, Ohio, near Toledo can be correlated through fossils with the Hamilton formation of New York State, the Traverse formation in Michigan and the Arkona shale of Southwestern Ontario. All were laid down in a Devonian period sea.

Almost never does a complete sequence of rocks in any region's geological history survive the wear and tear of earth's destructive processes. Rocks of an era or period may have disappeared or were never represented. By comparison with the rocks and fossils of other regions the missing strata can be accounted for. If igneous or metamorphic rocks are present, their age can be determined through isotopes of certain elements that decay or change their atomic structure at a measurable rate. In such ways an orderly accounting of a region's rock formations can be reckoned.

## How Fossils are Named

History would be unintelligible if Alexander the Great, Julius Caesar or William the Conqueror had been nameless. So it is with fossils. The fossil nomenclature is based on the Linnaean system, named for Carl Linnaeus, a Swede, who devised it in the early 1700s. This system uses Latin derivatives so that it can be understood by persons of any nation and language. It is an arbitrary classification that assigns a plant or animal to a species, the smallest grouping, and then assigns species into progressively larger categories. A species is a group of organisms similar to one another and capable of interbreeding and producing fertile offspring. A genus is a group of related species. Organisms are described by genus and species, such as genus *Homo* and species *sapiens* for man, and *Pecten ziczac* for a common scallop. The species and genus are printed in italics; the genus is capitalized. Except for that detail it is much like writing Doe, John, for a person. The larger groupings, in ascending order, are families, orders, classes and phyla. Man, for example, belongs to the phylum Chordata; subphylum Vertebrata; class Mammalia; order Primates, and family Hominidae.

Once in a while a creature emerges from the rocks and gives the paleontologists a bad time. Such is the Tully Monster, (Figure 84), which an oil refinery employe found while fishing south of Chicago and brought to the Field Museum. In the brown concretion from the strip coal mines lay the impression of a soft-bodied animal with fins and a spade-shaped tail, a bar across its body and a long probosis ending in a toothed claw. The stranger got name, *Tullimonstrum gregarium* (meaning common Tully monster, for its discoverer) but the monster didn't fit into any known phylum. So it is still a foundling in the fossil world.

As the museum scientists tried to do with the Tully Monster, the first step in identifying a fossil is to decide what phylum it belongs in. Is it a plant or an animal, a shell, a coral, or a fish? Clues include pearly shell, coiling, segmentation of body parts, symmetry, and pore structure. Once a tentative general identification has been arrived at, the amateur should go to illustrations in books about fossils of the area where it was found, or to local collections in museums and private hands.

Symmetry or lack of it is a useful clue, as indicated in Appendix 3, page 171. Symmetry can be either radial or bilateral. A wheel has radial

**84. This impression was left by the Tully monster in brown concretions in Illinois. A reconstruction of the soft-bodied creature is shown in Figure 16, page 19.**

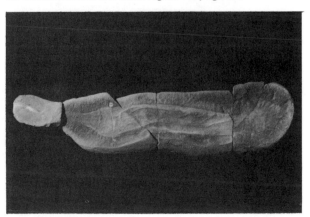

symmetry—repetition of its parts around an axis, so that any line through the axis would divide it into two identical pieces. Bilateral symmetry, however, requires duplication of parts that have right and left hand identity when the object is divided down the middle. A human face has this kind of symmetry. Many fossils, of course, possess neither kind of symmetry, and these, too, are listed in Appendix 3.

## Collecting Vertebrates

Amateurs usually confine their collecting to invertebrate fossils. There are two reasons. 1. Vertebrate fossils tend to be large and difficult to exhume and prepare for exhibition or study. 2. The federal Antiquities Act of 1906 limits collecting of some fossils, including such major vertebrate fossils as those of dinosaurs and mammoths, to recognized research institutions.

But few can resist being fascinated by dinosaurs. These Mesozoic reptiles dominated animal life for 100 million years until they became extinct about 70 million years ago. They came in all sizes and shapes. They swam like whales, flew like birds, grazed like cows, and ate other animals like tigers.

When dinosaur bones were discovered in the western United States, they became a battleground in the late 1870s and 1880s between two scholars, Othniel C. Marsh of Yale University and director of its Peabody Museum, and Edward D. Cope, of the University of Pennsylvania. Cope opened up dinosaur graveyards in New Mexico, near Canon City, Colorado, and in the Judith River area in Montana. Marsh sent his diggers to Como Bluff, Wyoming, and Morrison, Colorado, and defended his boneyards with rifles. Most of the fossils were in what is called the Morrison formation, a 200-foot thick stratum of hardened sand, mud and stream gravels, which turned out to be the world's richest source of dinosaur skeletons. Here, in what was once a lush marsh, the dinosaurs lived and died; their bones were preserved in desert sands that turned to stone as the Rockies rose.

Later the Carnegie Museum in Pittsburgh, the American Museum of Natural History, the National Museum of the Smithsonian Institution and the Field Museum in Chicago joined in the search. Dinosaurs were hunted in Canada, Asia and South America, and many new species were discovered. Even today, Brigham Young University in Utah digs for them on the western slope of the Rockies.

Vertebrate boneyards can be closer home than the wide open spaces of the West. Right in Los Angeles, off Wilshire Boulevard, lie the Rancho la Brea tar pits mentioned earlier in this chapter. Similar deposits exist at Carpinteria and McKittrick in California.

Ashy sediments at Fossil, Wyoming, can be split to reveal fish skeletons in delicate detail, like charcoal drawings on the soft warm brown stone. South Dakota's Badlands are happy hunting grounds for the skulls and bones of piglike oreodonts and other mammals. Near Cleveland, Ohio, excavation for Interstate 71 turned up 25 new species of fish that are exhibited by that city's Natural Science Museum.

These are only a few of the many places, especially in the Great Plains and the West, where the story of vertebrate evolution can be read in the rocks. Here the Mesozoic and Cenozoic rocks are near the surface. In the Midwest and much of the East, interest centers on the Paleozoic rocks with their invertebrate fossils.

Compared with invertebrate fossils, those of vertebrates are rare, just as we today have far more flies than elephants. Vertebrate remains should be left to the professionals. An amateur who discovers fossil bones, as many have, should notify a museum or university and then join with the professional team taking the fossils from the rock. His reward will be the opportunity to work with skilled scientists in the field. If the fossils he has found are those of a new species it may be named for him, as the Tully monster was named for Francis Tully. He may even be made an honorary associate of the museum. That is what happened to a plumber from San Jacinto who discovered bones in the Anza-Borrego Desert. He reported the location to the Los Angeles County Museum. The bones provided significant information on the geological history of southern California.

**85. Quartz geode from Tampa Bay, Florida, is a fossil replacement of coral.**

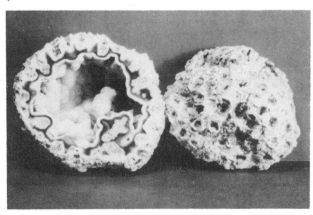

Some of the best discoveries have been made by the sharp eyes of youth. In a recent book, Dr. J. R. MacDonald of Los Altos, California, mentions Allan Bennison, a high schooler who found the vertebrae and skull of a hitherto unknown monasaur in the San Joaquin valley. It now bears Allan's name in its scientific name. A few years later, Allan discovered the first partial skeleton of a duck-billed dinosaur in Stanislaus County, California.

Bennet Day, son of a rancher in Shasta County, California, distinguished himself by discovering the first complete head of a superbison. Only the tip of one horn was visible, but careful excavation revealed that the horns were surrounded by a sandy cast of horn sheaths that measured 13½ feet from tip to tip.

America has not been as feverishly searched for the vertebrate ancestors of man as Africa, China and the Middle East. Anthropologists have long assumed that man first came here by way of the Bering Straits about 12,000 years ago. But recent excavation on a bluff above the Pacific near San Diego has uncovered bones and stone artifacts that suggest man lived there 40,000 to 50,000 years ago. That would be even before he reached Europe.

All fossils, not just vertebrate ones, help to establish our family tree. Alfred S. Romer, one of the world's most distinguished paleontologists, explains this in a brief review of how we got the way we are. Vertebrates, he writes, may have developed from invertebrates that became sexually mature while they were still in a free-swimming larval stage. Instead of settling down like the old folks to life on a stalk, they may have discovered how to evolve a bony skeleton and jaws like a fish, then grow legs to make the great leap to land, and lungs to breathe air. While their ancestors reproduced in water, the new forms could make themselves independent of water by developing the shelled egg. From this point, evolution into mammals and man would not be too far away.

Whatever the precise sequence of development may have been, the plants must have come before the animals. In nature's economy, animals cannot find food unless there are plants ready for them.

## What the Amateur Collects

The most primitive plants and animals cannot be clearly differentiated, but all are one-celled organisms that can be grouped under the name of protists. Not only are they the most ancient; they are also the most abundant. The protists include bacteria, algae, foraminifera whose skeletons built the White Cliffs of Dover, as well as giant kelp plants up to 150 feet long. Protists supply the basic food of all sea animals and they replenish the oxygen in the air we breathe. Scientists calculate that they take 150 billion tons of carbon and 25 billion tons of hydrogen annually from the air, and free 400 billion tons of oxygen for our lungs.

Fossil masses of algae and bacteria nearly 2 billion years old have been found near Lake Superior and at Saratoga Springs, New York, as well as in several other parts of the world. The Mary Ellen jasper in the mine of that name near Biwabik, Minnesota, is marked with swirls that are fossils of iron-secreting algae.

Tall tree ferns, scale trees, giant ancestors of modern horsetails, and the ancestors of the ginkgo and the conifers dominated the lush vegetation of the Paleozoic era's Pennsylvania period. They left a rich record of fern fronds and tree bark impressions in concretions, as well as other relics of the swamps that lay on the shores of invading seas. The rich deposits unearthed by the strip mines south of Chicago have provided collectors with millions of specimens. These concretions also bring to light the record of the hordes of insects, shrimp, jellyfish and worms that left their shadows as carbon impressions in the rocks.

Insects and plants seem to have moved onto the land together in the Devonian period, but fossils of insects are rare because thin wings and delicate legs do not survive well. Some insects were dramatic, though, such as the dragon fly with a 30-inch wingspread. Insects today out-

**86. Microspirifer brachiopods from Michigan resemble birds or butterflies in flight.**

number any other group of animals, but few of the Devonian types are included among living species. One of those, however, is the cockroach, which boasts a family tree 400 million years old. A living fossil, it can look on man as a rank newcomer.

Some fossil plants are as impressive as any dinosaur. Trees turned to stone may be seen today in the Petrified Forest National Park in Arizona, the Pike Petrified Forest on the west side of Pike's Peak in Colorado, and the standing forests in the back country of Yellowstone National Park. Washington state displays a magnificent variety of fossil trees in the Ginkgo Petrified Forest State Park near Vantage, and Mississippi shows its fossil forest near Flora. Leaves and fruit of Cenozoic plants and trees are preserved in the federally-protected ash beds near Florissant, Colorado, in the John Day basin, Oregon, and near Spokane, Washington.

Sponges, the first step up the evolutionary ladder from the protists, rarely make spectacular fossils, usually because only their spiny parts are preserved. But corals are another story. Corals belong to the phylum Coelenterata, which include such delightful forms as the Petoskey stone (Hexagonaria), found on Michigan beaches; horn corals; Favosites or honeycomb corals, and Halysites, which have a chainlike pattern. The beautiful quartz geodes from Florida are replacements of hexacoral, often known as brain coral (Figure 85). The sea fan which many vacationers bring home from Florida and the Caribbean is a coral, although unlike any of its relatives.

Only a few forms of the bryozoans, the next step up the ladder, are often collected, but they include Fenestrellina, a lacy fan, and its screwlike axis, Archimedes. Another ancient but more advanced phylum comprises the brachiopods, which are favorites of collectors because they are plentiful, occur in great variety of species, and often are beautiful. Brachiopods are bivalves, like clams, but unlike clams, their two shells are unlike in size and shape. One shell usually hangs over the other at the hinge, as is easily seen when the fossil is viewed from the side. From the front, however, they have bilateral symmetry (as illustrated in Appendix 3). Among the most gracefully-shaped brachiopods are the spirifers with their resemblance to a flying bird (Figure 86). They shared rule of the Paleozoic seas with the trilobites, then began to disappear in the Mesozoic era. But one species, Lingula, a small, smooth-shelled form, has survived essentially unchanged, like the cockroach, for 400 million years.

From the brachiopods it is an obvious evolutionary step to the Mollusc phylum, whose members live today in sea water, fresh water and on land. Most primitive are the chitons, whose shell is made up of strips of horny material. They live like the abalone anchored to a rock. Tusk shells are long and shaped like an elephant's tusk. The snails (gastropods) inhabit a single shell which is often twisted or fringed with spines. The clams (pelecypods), like the turtle "dwell neath plated decks," as the oyster demonstrates. Coal seams near Farmington, Illinois, have yielded handsome snails replaced by golden pyrite, much like the brachiopods similarly replaced that are found at Sylvania, Ohio (page 101). Missouri has also turned up clams replaced by reddish hematite.

### Quick-witted Octopus

Far more advanced are the cephalopods (Figure 87), which include the octopus, squid and nautilus as well as its extinct relatives, the ammonites and belemnites. The octopus and squid, the most intelligent of invertebrates, had the sense to discard the exterior shell and develop speed, keen insight and the ability to change color to help them survive. Ammonites have always been highly popular among collectors for their spiral shells that gleam in pearly, patterned splendor (page 101).

Worms are not well represented in fossil history except by their winding trails written in the rocks, but they are presumably ancestors of the next phylum, the arthropods, which include the trilobites. These are known in hundreds of species and in sizes from a quarter inch to more than two feet. Some trilobites are as unadorned as a Quaker spinster, some are fringed and bedecked like a dowager, but all are built on the same fundamental plan. The body consists of three segments running the length of the animal and divided by two furrows. These lobes are covered with a horny, jointed armor like that of a tumblebug. The head is often bedecked with a shield or collar, the body moves on jointed legs, and the tail segment may be rounded or taper to a point. Some species are blind, but some developed a complex set of highly efficient compound eyes that may occupy most of the face. Sylvania, Ohio, Lemont, Illinois, Milwaukee, Wisconsin, Antelope Springs, Utah, western British Columbia, and several places in New York State are famous collecting sites.

The relationship of other arthropods—the crabs, lobsters, shrimp, scorpions and insects—to trilobites is easy to see, for they have a hard

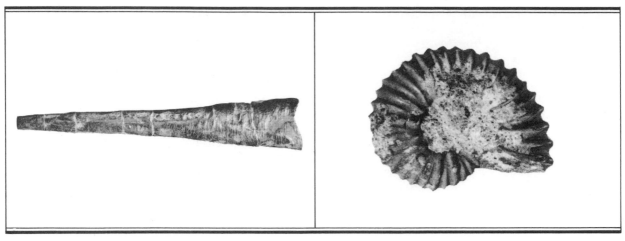

**87. Straight and curved forms are cephalopods, which also include the octopus, squid and pearly nautilus.**

outer skeleton like their ancestor (Figures 76 and 77). Many of these turn up in the fossil record, such as the eurypterid family of giant scorpions up to several feet long, which must have been terrors of Silurian seas. Notable places for collecting eurypterids are near Manchester, Ohio, and in New York State. Insects, which presumably were the first animals to leave the sea for the land, today are the largest single group with perhaps a million species. They still adapt quickly and flourish in almost any earthly environment.

Unlike the insects, the next phylum stayed in the sea. These are the echinoderms, including the collector's favorite, the crinoid. These flower-like animals, often called sea lilies, grew in colonies in the sea, anchored to the bottom by long, flexible, jointed stems. On these stems swayed the bodies, fashioned of tiny calcite plates, from which protruded feathery, petal-like arms that swept floating bits of food into the crinoid's mouth. Museums are kept busy identifying the stem segments for people who have found them on beaches. They are also called Indian beads.

A limestone quarry near LeGrand, Iowa, was so rich in crinoids and other sea life fossils that it led one youngster, Burnice H. Beane, into a lifetime hobby of collecting (Figure 83). One 3-by-5 foot slab from the quarry contained 183 starfish, 12 sea urchins, two trilobites and a crinoid. For more than 40 years Beane used a brush and needle to painstakingly clean and expose the details of crinoids and starfish in rocks from the quarry, discovering many new crinoid species in the process. Today, LeGrand crinoid slabs are in museums in Capetown, London, Paris, Tokyo, and several large American cities.

Another dedicated crinoid collector was Charles Beachler, who in 1886 when he was 15 years old hand set and printed a small book about the famous crinoids found in the soft limestone along the local stream banks in Crawfordsville, Indiana. At the same time, Mary P. Haines was collecting and cataloguing her several hundred fossils, including crinoids, that she had found in nearby Richmond, Indiana. Today her collection lies in the Field Museum along with those of many celebrated scientists.

Blastoids (which are much like crinoids but lack arms), starfish, sand dollars and sea urchins are among the collectible echinoderms.

## A Missing Link?

Beyond echinoderms lie the mysterious graptolites, which get their name from their resemblance to black markings on rock. These were floating colonies that have some claim to being the missing link between the invertebrates and the vertebrates because they appear to have something like a rudimentary spinal cord. Collecting them is usually left to specialists who have mastered the technical difficulty of working with their fragile remains.

This is the fossil story, a story whose beginnings are barely decipherable in the record of the rocks, then suddenly exciting with a burst of life forms in the Paleozoic era. Then came the dramatic extinction of the trilobites and the dinosaurs, and the steady progression toward man. George Gaylord Simpson, distinguished Yale University paleontologist, sums it up well by saying that through fossils "our minds...can range through the past and see all the curious creatures and scenes of life's history in ever-changing sequence."

# The magic of fluorescence

When dull rocks glow in vivid colors under certain wavelengths of ultraviolet light, the phenomenon is called fluorescence. The rays that generate this colorful response are invisible, which is why the lamps that emit them are called black lights. As explained in Chapter Five, miners and collectors use the lights to locate and identify certain minerals, whose color response will vary with the mineral's location. Gemologists use black lights to distinguish between many natural and synthetic gemstones, and with such precision they can often tell who manufactured the synthetic. The photos at bottom, left, supplied by Ultra-Violet Products, Inc., show some fluorescent mineral specimens under natural light. The photos immediately below show the same specimens under shortwave fluorescent light. The captions below identify the minerals in each specimen.

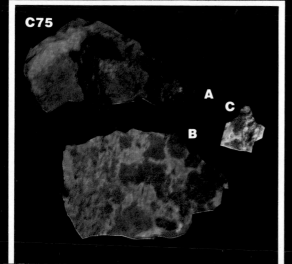

C75. Left, under natural daylight it is difficult to distinguish the various minerals in these samples. Specimens a and b are from Franklin, New Jersey. Specimen c is from Greenland.

C76. Above. under shortwave ultraviolet light, specimen a is revealed as a rare specimen containing willemite (green), calcite (red), hardystonite (blue) and esperite (yellow). The black areas are franklinite which does not fluoresce. Specimen b displays the brilliant green fluorescence of willemite and brilliant red fluorescence of calcite typical of fine specimens found in the Franklin, New Jersey area. The brilliant red areas in specimen c are fluorescing tugtupite, a sodium beryllium aluminum silicate chloride related to the sodalite minerals group. It was first found in Greenland in 1957. The areas fluorescing white and pale gold in this specimen are sodalite, and the blue areas are a reflection of light from the shortwave lamp.

113

# Identifying earth and moon minerals

Minerals have an inner beauty artists would appreciate but rarely see. When polarized light passes through wafer-thin, translucent slices of minerals, the optical properties of different minerals produce characteristic color patterns, as these photographs from E. Leitz, Inc. show. Scientists use microscopes with rotating stages, polarized light, and gypsum plates to make such identifications as these:

C77. Left, above. In this moon rock, the elongated, striped red, blue and yellow minerals are plagioclase feldspars, the patterned red crystal in the lower right corner is cristobalite, and the black areas are ilmenite.

C78. Left. The elongated, lath-like gray mineral in this moon sample is twinned plagioclase feldspar; the reddish-orange mineral is pyroxene.

C79. Below. This is not Dante's Inferno but a wafer-thin slice of calcite augite feldspar, photographed through a polarizing microscope.

Opposite page.

C80. Top, left. The long bladed minerals in this earth sample of schist are biotite, and the blue to dark gray areas are quartz. Black areas are extinction positions—where the mineral won't pass light as the microscope stage is rotated.

C81. Top, right. The colorful minerals are pyroxenes with some olivine. The line running diagonally toward upper left is a micropegmatite of gabbro.

C82. Bottom, left. The vivid colors in this slice of earth rock are pyroxenes. The black areas are pyroxenes in the extinction position.

C83. Bottom, right. The blue, red and yellow minerals are serpentinized olivine (the yellow alterations are the serpentine). Lath-like minerals are plagioclase which is twinned, producing the striped appearance.

C79

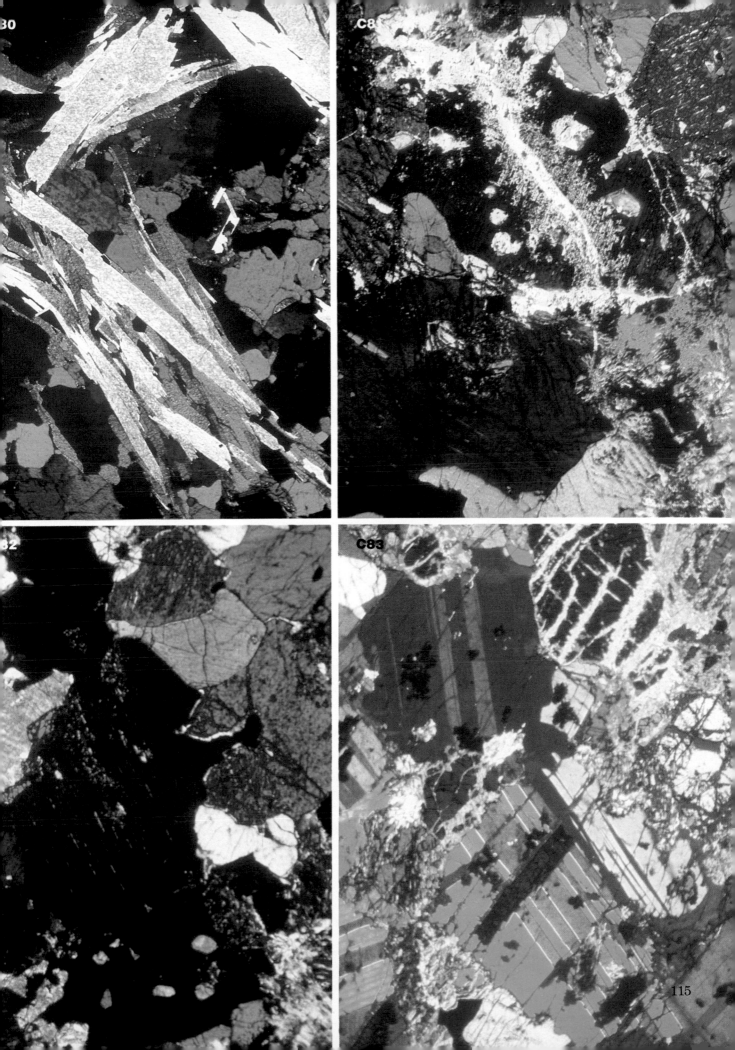

C80

C81

C82

C83

115

# The craftsmen's way with minerals

An infinite variation in colors and patterns tempts craftsmen to fashion minerals into something more than jewelry. Professional artisans use special tools to make the intricate carvings shown on these pages. But beginners can make attractive projects with minerals, too, using the plans and techniques given in Chapter Nine. Some good projects for beginners are shown on pages 119 and 120.

C84.   Below. Chinese temple lion carved from malachite poses beside polished piece of malachite. The two show the banded and orbicular (rounded) patterns typical of this mineral, which is softer and more readily carved than jade.

C84

C85. Top. The colorful birds are carved from various shades and patterns of jasper and agate, and posed with a background of petrified wood. Carving hard minerals, such as these examples from Idar-Oberstein, Germany, is done with specially shaped drills or abrasive bits.

C86. Left. The 14½-inch-tall Big John fluorite vase from Derbyshire, England, is a masterpiece of craftsmanship. Relatively soft fluorite can be shaped more readily than harder minerals, but special abrasive tools are needed to hollow out the interiors of vases and bottles.

C87. Another example of fine German craftsmanship is the white herons standing on a polished slab of petrified wood that looks like dark green water. The birds' bodies are carved from the mineral howilite.

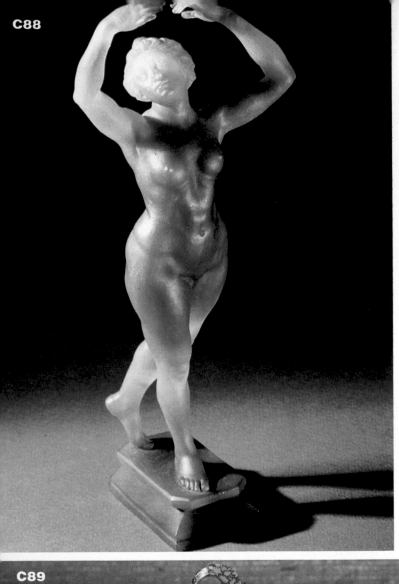

**C88**

C88. Left. This 10-inch high figurine was once a block of unusually perfect translucent chalcedony, found in Uruguay, South America. Called *Pas de Danse,* It was painstakingly carved by the eminent French sculptor and gem engraver, Georges Tonnelier.

C89. Below. Unpolished and polished nuggets of turquoise, foreground, and Chinese ox carved from spider web turquoise, background, show some of this mineral's natural colors. The most valuable are the bluest ones, but inferior stones are often treated with oil, wax or plastics to improve their colors. If turquoise "sweats" when left in the sun, suspect a treatment.

Opposite page.

C90. Top, left. Window rack is an easy project for craftsmen who want to display their translucent minerals. Construction information is given in Chapter Nine and Figure 136, page 154.

C91. Top, right. To craft mineral eggs and spheres, follow the instructions given on page 153. Eggs on stands are red agate and green marble; those in foreground are brassy pyrite and pink rhodochrosite. Sphere is shaped from granite.

C92. Center, left. An attractive pair of bookends can be made by sawing a chunk of patterned mineral in two, and then polishing, as explained in Chapter Nine. These were made from a large chalcedony filled geode.

C93. Center, right. Mythological lion dogs and stylized plant forms ornament this jade censer from China, which was carved several hundred years ago. Such intricate carvings, on an object just over 6 inches in diameter, show why master craftsmen delight in working with this tough, fibrous gem mineral.

C94. Polished mineral slices convert readily into clocks or bases for desk pen holders, using commercial clock movement and pen holder kits (see page 155 and Figure 139).

C95. Bottom, right. Even the bark pattern is retained in this large slice of petrified, agatized wood. It makes a fine book end or display specimen.

**C89**

**C90**

**C91**

**C92**

**C93**

**C94**

**C95**

119

C96. Top, left. Slices of translucent minerals fixed with epoxy to a sheet of glass or plastic, then set into a frame, make colorful divider screens. They don't have to be as large or elaborate as this example from the Funk Museum in Shirley, Illinois.

C97. Top, right. Slices of opaque but colorful minerals can be embedded in plastic or cement and mounted in a table top framed of angle iron. The technique of embedding the minerals is described on page 155.

C98. Center, left. One way to display your tumbled gem minerals is to use them in a lamp like this. Instructions for making it are given on pages 159 and 160.

C99. Directly above. A spray of branching copper, fixed in a discarded fisherman's cork float, makes a charming table or mantle decoration.

C100. Far left. Fragments of carnelian, amethyst and other translucent minerals form this cross designed by Dr. Dearing Lewis of Tucson, Arizona. Fixed to a pane of glass with epoxy, the cross was then framed in wrought iron and placed on a window sill where the sun would light up the cross.

C101. Left. Slices of jasper divided by many small chips of turquoise were embedded in plastic to form this table top, designed by William G. Allen of Thousand Palms, California.

*Chapter VII*

# Hunting for Minerals, Gems, Ores or Fossils

*"Nothing's so hard but search will find it out."*
—Herrick

Years ago John A. Grenzig, a highly respected collector and mineral dealer in Brooklyn, had a dream. He dreamed that he had gone to a quarry in West Paterson, New Jersey, found a boulder there, borrowed a sledge that was leaning against the quarry office and split the rock with one blow. To his surprise, he saw before him "two halves of a 3-by-5-inch amethyst geode."

Grenzig told his wife about the dream. At her urging he took the morning train to West Paterson and walked to the quarry. Sure enough, inside lay a boulder like the one he had dreamed about. He borrowed a sledge leaning against the shed, split the boulder with one blow, and before him lay the two halves of the amethyst geode he had dreamed about, just as he had pictured it.

Only a skeptic would doubt such a good story. Unfortunately, dreaming is not the way most collectors find good specimens. The real secret is preparation. It starts by visiting museums, shows and mineral club meetings where one becomes familiar with the appearance of minerals and fossils, and of the rock formations and matrices in which they are likely to be found. Then one learns of good collecting areas from mineral magazines, pamphlets and books such as are listed in Appendix 4, and by attending mineral club meetings and talking to collectors there.

Many state tourist bureaus and geological surveys provide publications giving descriptions and locations of state minerals or fossils free for the asking. It is wise to start with these, since good specimens may be closer than you think. Gold has been found only 15 miles northwest of Washington, D.C. and the American Museum of Natural History has a 6-inch garnet found in an excavation at 35th Street and Broadway in New York City. In fact, J.G. Manchester wrote a small book about the minerals found in the rocky foundations of Manhattan.

Other sources of information about collecting areas are members of mineral clubs who live in those areas, and a list of such clubs and their officers is published in the annual Buyers Guide issue of the Lapidary Journal. Write the clubs for guidance and suggestions. You should also obtain maps of the area, service station road maps that show you how to get there and back, and, equally important, topographic quadrangle maps of the collecting site published by the United States Geological Survey. By contour lines, symbols and color, the topographic maps show all natural features, such as hills, valleys and streams, as well as place names, roads, buildings and civil land divisions (Figure 89).

Maps for regions east of the Mississippi river can be purchased from the U.S.G.S. Distribution branch, 1200 S. Eads St., Arlington, Virginia, 22202; those for areas west of the Mississippi river from the Distribution Center in the Federal Center, Denver, Colorado, 80225. Lists of other U.S.G.S.publications can be obtained from the same addresses, as can a free index to the quadrangle maps that show topographical contours. Maps of national forests are published by the U.S. Forest Service, Washington, D.C. 20415. For quadrangle maps for Canada, write the Geological Survey of Canada, Ottawa.

**88. Members of a Chicago mineral club use geologist's hammers and a sledge with chisels for splitting off rocks containing specimens.**

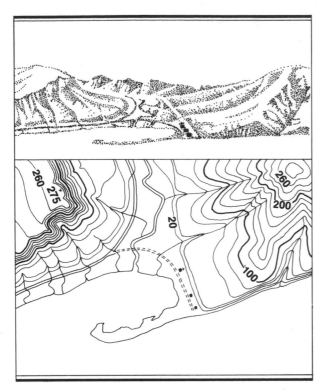

**89. How a landscape looks when plotted on a contour map. Each contour line represents areas that are at a certain level. Lines are far apart where land is flat or gently sloping, close together where land rises steeply.**

The only feature of the quadrangle maps that may puzzle some users is the contour lines to indicate elevation, in effect, a third dimension on a flat, two-dimension surface. Each line represents an imaginary line on the ground that follows a constant elevation above sea level. Contour lines will be far apart on a flat plain or gentle slope, and bunched together tightly where a hill or cliff rises abruptly (Figure 89).

Make sure your collecting site can be reached readily in the time allotted, with plenty of time left for prospecting. Nothing is more frustrating than to find a ledge of beautiful quartz crystals—or one teeming with trilobites—and have no time left to harvest them before you must return home.

A couple living in Klamath Falls, Oregon, shows what can be done by using time skillfully. Both have to work six days but the car is packed the night before they leave. They start promptly at 5 p.m. Saturday, drive until midnight and sleep at the predetermined collecting site. They are up at daybreak, look over the site, then have breakfast and hunt until early afternoon. Along the way back they stop at one or two other sites and arrive back home at 1 a.m.

Monday. With such limited time, by careful planning they have collected all over southern Oregon, northern California and northwestern Nevada in just a few years of weekends.

## What You Will Need

When you know where you are going, how to get there and what to look for when you do, the battle is more than half won. Only details remain, such as what to take and what to wear. Most trips will be made in an automobile, camper or trailer. The vehicle should be in good shape, recently serviced and equipped with dependable tires. If the collecting site is far from paved roads and service stations, as many are in the west, take several spare tires, tire pump, chicken wire for traction in sand or mud, a tow rope, extra fan belts and cans for water and fuel.

Keep a flashlight, compass and first aid kit in the car along with a sun screen to prevent sunburn. A small amount of meat tenderizer may ease any bee stings, and sulphur dusted in clothing may discourage chiggers. For snack rations, raisins, chocolate and fruit juice are ideal.

The tool most used by prospectors is the geologist's hammer, which has a square striking face and a pointed pick face (Figure 90). The hammer is used to break small rocks, drive chisels and pry strata apart. One chisel should be pointed, with a four-square face, and others should have blade faces. For heavier work, a sledge and long pry bar are needed. Depending on the terrain, a pick and shovel, rock scoop, rake, coarse screen for sorting gravel and a fine one for sifting sand may be useful. Some gold prospectors find a gold pan, sniping tool, whiskbroom, tweezers, spoon, magnet, small jar and old blanket worthwhile additions (Figure 91). A strong knife always finds a thousand uses. Fossil collectors may need a small can of acrylic spray or lacquer to protect delicate specimens.

Paper for wrapping specimens, cotton for packing delicate ones, bags, boxes, adhesive labels to mark specimens, a pencil and a notebook for data—all these help assure a safe journey home for your treasures, and provide a record of their origin when they get there. The careful collector knows just where each specimen came from, and when he collected it, and he doesn't do it from memory. He makes his notes as he collects and puts the record with each specimen as he packs it.

Clothing is more easily adjusted to the weather and time of day if it is worn in layers—shirts, sweaters and a jacket and raincoat. It should be loose, made of smooth material and should cover the whole body—arms, legs and head. You don't see the Bedouins, who live in the desert, riding their camels bare-headed and in shorts. Slacks for both men and women are comfortable and convenient. In quarries and mines a hard hat, safety shoes and safety glasses are required by law. Army-type high shoes are adequate for most collecting situations. They support and protect the ankles and are sturdy enough to stand up in mud, rocky places and sand. Boots are too heavy, and rocks soon chew up canvas shoes. Leather gloves save you from many a cut and blister when you are working with rocks. Wear spectacles and sun glasses that are shatter resistant and take along a hat that will really shield the face.

## Ideal Locations

Few amateur collectors have the time or resources to do much more than scratch the earth's surface when prospecting. The best locations for them to try are areas where the rock is exposed naturally, as it is in a quarry, mine dump, gravel pit, railroad or highway cut, building excavation, beach or stream gravel deposit, or a rock-strewn desert.

**90. Knapsack, geologist's hammer, chisel, knife, pencil, tape, magnifier and paper for wrapping specimens are collecting essentials. A sledge, additional chisels, shovel, pry bar, rake, and some of the other materials noted in the text may come in handy.**

Quarries are prime collecting areas, especially in regions deeply buried under glacial debris, such as the middle western United States. Limestone quarries frequently strike fossiliferous strata, and quarries in granite or metamorphic rocks may expose desirable minerals. Most quarries limit collecting to week-ends or other times when their work force is not present. The Foote mine in North Carolina, for example, is open to collectors one day a month, and the Limecrest quarry in New Jersey welcomes them one day a year.

Few are as cooperative as one where the New York Mineralogical club "planted" labeled specimens so that none of its members would go home empty handed. Occasionally an outsider who ran across a specimen left behind after a club trip there would marvel at the consideration of a quarry that labeled its discarded rocks for his convenience.

Most quarries restrict collecting to the dumps; a few will permit entry after a blast has exposed fresh material. The key to successful collecting, therefore, is to become familiar with the rocks of the quarry and learn to recognize the strata that contain desired specimens when they appear in the blasted material or the dumps.

## Brief Baedeker for Collectors

Of the thousands of quarries in the United States, only a few can be mentioned here. Georgia has its famous marble quarries at Tate, and Alabama's marble comes from Sylacauga. New Jersey's quarries at Paterson, Great Notch and Upper Montclair, to mention only a few, have long provided desirable zeolites and other min-

**91. Gold panners find these additional tools helpful.**

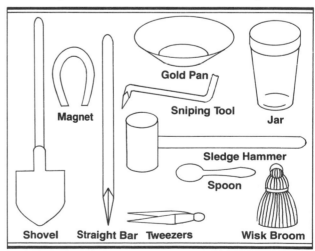

erals, and New York quarries garnet at Gore Mountain for abrasives and some gem material. Amateurs dig in the dolomite ledges around Little Falls and Middleville in New York State for the small glistening quartz crystals known as "Herkimer diamonds." Vermont is called the Granite State for its quarries at Barre from which come many of the nation's tombstones. The state is equally renowned for the marbles of Rutland.

Farther west the limestone foundations of the middle west in Ohio, Indiana, Illinois and Iowa reward diligent collectors. Ohio has quarries, sources of fossils, calcite and celestite, at Sylvania, Custar and Woodville, as well as its gem flint, the finest in the world, which is quarried from Flint Ridge between Zanesville and Newark. The Indians used the flint for arrowheads; we dig it for jewelry. Indiana has quarries at Rensselaer, Francesville and Logansport, notable for pyrite and fossils. Another quarry is farther south at Waldron, the famous oolitic limestone quarries are at Bloomington and Bedford, and there's a quarry in a probable meteor crater at Kentland. Illinois quarries, like those of Iowa, afford crystal-lined geodes as well as famous crinoid and starfish fossils. The strip mines south of Chicago still yield fern and animal fossils in clay ironstone nodules.

Farther west, Colorado has marble quarries at a town of that name, and Wyoming quarries fossil fish slabs at a town of that name. Turritella agate, which is neither agate nor turritella fossil shells, is dug near Wamsutter, Wyoming, and fossils of Ice Age animals can be seen at the tar pits in downtown Los Angeles.

Like quarries, mine dumps are profitable places to look for minerals. Old dumps are usually more rewarding than newer ones because mines were first opened near the surface in richly mineralized ground and under primitive conditions that caused the miners to discard all except the richest ore. Many modern mines sort ore inside the mine and never bring any rock to the surface except when they are cutting shafts or passages in barren ground. So concentrate on locating the most promising dumps, including the dumps from prospect holes where mining was started but abandoned as unpromising. Dumps are easier to search after a rain has washed the rock and made the crystals visible. Old ore bins and mine buildings may repay a search for specimens overlooked by busy miners.

California's ghost towns and piles of gravel from the giant dredges remain for collectors to search. And snorkelers and scuba divers, as well as amateur gold panners are finding gold in California streams, as they are in such other gold states as Colorado, Georgia and North Carolina. Cripple Creek and Central City were highlights in Colorado's golden years, along with the silver bonanzas at Leadville, and at Silverton, where rhodochrosite and tungsten minerals still turn up in the dumps. Today the molybdenum mine at Climax is popular, but there are many old mine sites worth visiting, such as those at Salida and westward to Gunnison and Ouray. Farther north lies Virginia City, Nevada, and the traces of its silver glories.

Nearby Arizona has extensive dumps at the United Verde mine at Jerome, the open pit workings at Globe, Bisbee and Tiger, and the obsidian nodules known as Apache tears at Ray, itself a famous mining town. Don't miss the magnificent red cliffs of Sedona, Sunset Craters at Flagstaff, many historic Indian cliff dwellings and the Grand Canyon and the great Meteor crater near Winslow. In New Mexico the old turquoise mines at Los Cerrillos, the colorful minerals of the dumps at Magdalena, the mines near Bingham, and the serpentine in the dumps at Silver City may repay a visit. So will the White Sands National Monument near Alamagordo. Montana has many mines, but none so memorable as the great copper workings at Butte, now partly an open pit operation.

Arkansas mines splendid quartz crystal groups in the Ouachita mountains between Norman and Crystal Springs, and its Magnet Cove workings are indeed a magnet for collectors of rare minerals. Arkansas also has the only diamond mine in the United States (page 57) now open to the public, and its streams still yield gem quality freshwater pearls.

Missouri is the nation's principal source of barite, and lead and zinc ores are mined around Potosi, Joplin and a new district near Salem. Its golden calcite crystals are prized in collections around the world. Not far away, Illinois mines fluorite as well as beautiful barite and calcite formations from deposits that lie along the Ohio river near Cave in Rock. Similar deposits in Kentucky extend into the area of Marion.

Wisconsin's iron deposits, now depleted, were centered in its far north around Hurley and Ironwood, Michigan, where they join Michigan's mine belt east from Crystal Falls to Ishpeming and Marquette. At Ishpeming jaspalite—striped hematite and jasper—is collected for ornamental uses, such as bookends, and so is the colorful Kona dolomite. In addition to Michigan's old copper mines on Keweenaw peninsula and farther south on the mainland, there are active workings in the salt deposits under Detroit and

Windsor, Ontario, and in the gypsum mines at Grand Rapids. Wisconsin looms as a major copper producer from new prospects near Crandon, south of the iron ranges. From southern Wisconsin and Illinois came the lead ores which gave their name to the city of Galena, Illinois. Old mine dumps are plentiful around Mineral Point, Wisconsin, and nearby in Illinois.

Dumps from Minnesota's old mines around Hibbing, Virginia and Soudan are not hard to find. Pennsylvania was until a few years ago a major iron producer with its huge mine at Cornwall, which has been closed. In New Jersey, zinc mining continues at Sterling Hill, but the famous Franklin mine is now a memory kept alive by the devotion of collectors to its Buckwheat and Trotter dumps.

Pebbles and boulders on bars in rivers, beaches and gravel pits are rich sources of agates, petrified wood and bone, and other weather-resistant fossils. Stream gravels tend to preserve only the hard, fine-grained rocks—such as quartz and its relatives—that can survive the stream abrasion. Like gold, the heavy minerals, such as corundum and garnet, settle to the bottom or in cracks and crannies in the beds of running streams.

A prime example is provided by the wealth of sapphires taken from streams in Montana, notably at Helena from the Missouri river bars, and at Philipsburg. Idaho's star garnets are dug from the bottom of Emerald Creek near Fernwood. Montana's fancifully patterned moss agates come from the ranches along the banks of the Yellowstone river from Billings to Sidney.

Oregon and Washington beaches have been favorite collecting places for years for agate and petrified wood, as has the ocean front in many parts of California, notably at Jade Cove, south of Monterey. New Mexico's "Pecos diamonds" are doubly terminated quartz crystals picked from the Pecos river in New Mexico, and Cape May quartz "diamonds" come from the beach sands at Cape May, New Jersey.

The Rio Grande valley in Texas, especially at Falcon Dam, is rich in agate and petrified wood pebbles. Farther east is a bonanza for the beachcomber in Florida's Hillsborough Bay agatized coral near Tampa, Naples and its fossil shark's teeth, and the manatee bones and other fossils in the phosphate beds at Bartow. The dumps along the Cross-Florida canal, now abandoned, and other excavations in northern Florida are good places to hunt for fossil shells and bones.

The Midwest's Father of Waters, the Mississippi River, is also the father of agates. From the gravel pits along its course through Minnesota, Wisconsin, Iowa and Illinois, as well as farther south, many thousands of gaily-striped Lake Superior agates have been recovered. Minnesota's Mille Lacs district is also a favorite hunting ground for these gems. Michigan's Keweenaw county beaches offer delightful beachcombing for its elusive agates and prehnite pebbles washed up by Lake Superior. From farther south in the same state, near Petoskey, come the prized fossil corals known as Petoskey stones.

In Wyoming, jade is still found sometimes in the hills around Lander and Jeffrey City, and petrified wood at Wiggins Fork. The high plains of South Dakota and Nebraska north of Crawford are strewn with chalcedony pebbles. Among them is an occasional Fairburn agate named for the town near which they were first found. South Dakota also provides a wealth of vertebrate fossils as well as examples of ammonites and the rare cycad, a primitive plant. Like South Dakota, Nebraska has petrified wood and fossils for those who search its streams, stony fields and gravel pits.

Colorado's petrified wood is scattered throughout the countryside south of Denver and along the border with Utah and westward in the Colorado Plateau. Fruita in Utah is a favorite collecting area. Central Washington has great resources of fossil wood around Vantage and a fine museum there to show the variety of its species. Madras, Sweet Home, Prineville and Antelope are among the Oregon localities for collecting the nodules of agate and opal, called thundereggs, that erode from the lava plains. Prineville welcomes visitors with collecting tours and an annual rock-hunting festival. Nearby are the Glass Buttes, crags of varicolored obsidian. The John Day country south of Pendleton is known for the variety of its fossils.

Idaho has a rhyolite known as wonderstone near Fallon and petrified wood near Coaldale, and Nevada has petrified wood just beyond Montgomery Pass on the California line near Bishop.

Many localities for gathering agate and jasper exist in the California deserts near Mojave, Barstow and Needles, and farther south is a favorite locality for agate at Wiley Well. Boron minerals can be collected at Boron. Clifton and Safford in the mountains of eastern Arizona and Deming, N.M., have long yielded agate and nodules. Although you can't collect in the Petrified Forest, a showcase of fossil woods, collecting is easy on ranches nearby. A broad sweep of Texas is strewn with fossil wood, and the agates on ranches around Alpine attract thousands yearly. The barite "roses" of Norman, Oklahoma, and the fantastic gypsum crystals from the Salt Plains east of Cherokee in the same state are classics among minerals.

### The Rich Pegmatites

Many gem minerals are found in pegmatites which occur in the form of long, slender dikes made up of coarse crystalline materials, mainly quartz and feldspars. Collectors search for crystal-lined cavities, carefully clean clay and loose crystals from the cavity, then pry sections of its wall free to remove the attached crystals on their matrix.

South Dakota's pegmatite deposits near Rapid City are remarkable for their huge masses of rose quartz, phosphate minerals and large plates of mica. Those of Colorado around Florissant and to the north have long been a source of museum-quality groups of green amazonite with smoky quartz. The pegmatites in Mason County, Texas, also produce blue topaz of gem quality. Colorado's other well-known pegmatite region is near Canon City.

From California's pegmatites in the Pala and Ramona area have come a fantastic number of fine tourmaline crystals, the spodumene kunzite, and quartz, beryl and garnet. Oxford County in southwest Maine is California's major rival for tourmaline with famous mines near Newry, Paris and Rumford. North Carolina's pegmatites around Spruce Pine have been worked for gems, and those near King's Mountain for industrial minerals. Other Carolina gem sources are found near Franklin, where tourists may wash rubies, sapphires and rhodolite garnets from mud dug in the Cowee creek valley, and at Abbeville, South Carolina, noted for its fine amethyst.

Virginia is the source of green and pink unakite from Warren, Page and Rockbridge counties and staurolites—fairy crosses—from Patrick County. Amazonite and garnet from Amelia, Virginia, also appear in many collections, as do specimens from the mineral-rich pegmatites of Haddam Neck and Portland, in Connecticut, and the mines at North Groton, Grafton Center and Moat Mountain near North Conway, New Hampshire.

A new development that makes collecting easier has been the growth of areas open for a fee and often with a limit on the amount that can be collected. The numerous ruby placer mines along Cowee creek near Franklin, North Carolina, and the sapphire diggings in Montana are examples. In the November 1976 *Lapidary Journal* about 75 fee areas in the eastern states

were listed, with addresses and other data about them. Another list of 100 western fee areas appeared in the December issue. Fees help the owner keep up his property and make it more accessible to the collector.

At least two states have opened rockhound parks. New Mexico's is near Deming with quite a long list of agate and other goodies for the taking, and the Iowa area of 800 acres of former strip mine dumps is near Knoxville, with fossils, petrified wood and calcite as the attractions.

### Some Prospecting Lore

One successful collector often earned the envy of his fellows on a field trip by coming up with specimens while they were empty handed. When asked his secret he confessed that he looked over the collecting site, then wandered away and often came across a forgotten mine dump or unworked rock face. Such tactics enabled him to score at the popular Line Pits on the Pennsylvania-Maryland state line, where he found good serpentine in a pile of rocks left by the miners in the woods, and at King's Mountain in North Carolina where he traced a vague seam of tour-

**92. For specimens too large to take home, chisel a channel around the desired portion, always letting the force of the blows be away from the specimen. When the channel is deep enough, a few taps should free the specimen from the matrix rock in which it is embedded.**

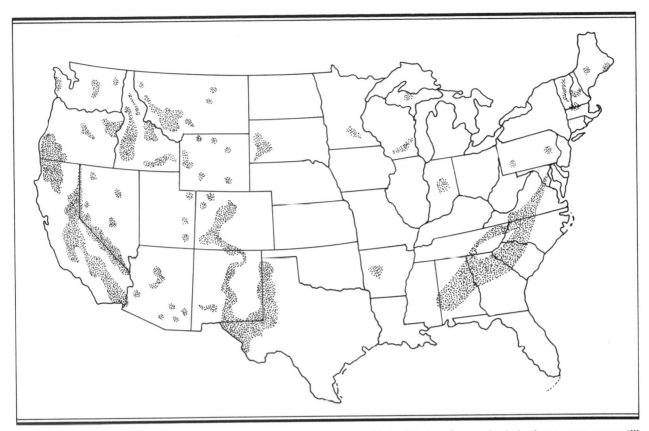

93. The dotted areas show major placer or loose gold deposits in the United States. Stream beds in these areas may still contain gold.

maline to a pocket of crystals. He advised his friends to be nosy and inquisitive. While it is still true that the place to collect is where others have found good specimens, it pays to range wider, dig deeper and work harder.

Freeways are often cut through tempting rock formations, but it is usually impossible to stop close enough to gain access to them. Side roads from them may lead to equally good areas, however. The piles of rubble at the foot of hills and mountains (called talus) are rewarding locations because the specimens are close at hand and the rock may offer clues to better things above. Carl Anderson found his lapis lazuli mine near Gunnison, Colorado, in this way. He rolled boulders down from various levels on Italian Mountain until some stopped near where he had found a fragment of lapis. On the level from which he had rolled the stone was the ledge with lapis lazuli he was seeking.

Don't ignore areas that have been searched before. Flooding streams can bring down or uncover new minerals or fossils. And loose stones raised from the ground by frost action are rich sources of agates, petrified wood and bone, and other weather-resistant fossils. Examples are the famous Kansas chalk beds, moss agate nodules that turn up every year on Montana ranch lands, and the Lake Superior agates that come from the gravels in the Mississippi River or from Minnesota fields and gravel pits.

### Desert Varnish, White Skins and "Slicks"

Pebbles on the ground, particularly in regions of little rain, tend to disguise themselves with a mahogany colored coating called desert varnish, or they may weather white from surface alteration (Figure 14, page 18). Jade hunters have learned to look for the green wind-polished tips of buried rocks called "slicks." Or they break or chip small rocks to see if they have the green color and hackly fracture characteristic of jade. Agates may also have a dull coating that hides their beauty and petrified wood may be crazed with tiny cracks or flaws. Learning to recognize the various surface disguises is the key to a successful search.

If a specimen is in a rocky matrix that is too large to be taken home, there is a technique for removing it from the matrix. Chisel a channel around the specimen, placing the chisel in such a position that the hammer blows strike away from the specimen (Figure 92). When the channel is deep enough so that the specimen is isolated on a pedestal, a careful tap or two at the base of the pedestal should free the specimen intact. Protect any crumbling fossils with a coat of acrylic spray.

### Special Tips on Gold Prospecting

Finding a vein of gold-bearing quartz is a real thrill but a rare one. Most gold found by amateurs is *placer* gold—loose metal deposits in the dirt or gravel of streambeds. Water wears gold-bearing quartz from the matrix rock and washes it into the stream. As the rock moves downstream it breaks up, freeing gold flakes and nuggets from the quartz. The gold—which is much heavier than lead—sinks, gradually working its way down through silt, sand and gravel until it reaches bedrock. Look for it there, in both wet or dry streambeds.

Likely spots are the slow-moving side of streams and wherever eddies might allow the heavy gold to sink. Probe for cracks or crevices in the streambed or bedrock where the gold may deposit. Gold may also be around the base of boulders that interrupted the water flow. Work below the line of the high water mark, which is usually visible even in dry stream beds. If the bed is dry, dig or brush away loose dirt or sand to

94.  In working a dry creek bed for gold, brush away sand and gravel to discover cracks. Probe bottom of these cracks with a pick or the sniping tool, shown here, spooning out material into gold pan to be panned with water later.

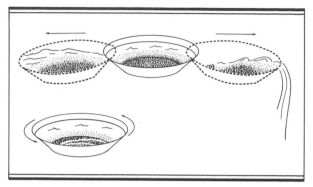

95.  With pan half full of sand and gravel, dip in water, shake back and forth vigorously to separate material, then fill with water and pan as explained in text.

locate the crevices, then work material out of them with a geologist's pick or sniping tool (Figure 94). Transfer the material to a gold pan with a spoon until the pan is one-half full.

(A word about that pan: amateurs prefer a 16-inch pan with sloping sides that are 2½ inches high. Its surface should not be too smooth so they usually give it a scorching or weathering treatment to obtain a slightly roughened texture.)

### Panning the Gold

With the pan half full of material, dip it in the stream to drench the dirt (Figure 95), stir, remove large pebbles, and shake the pan back and forth thoroughly. This helps segregate the contents by weight. Then fill the gold pan with water and rotate and wobble it slightly so that some water spills over the side, carrying with it dirt and other lighter material. Dip, swirl and wobble repeatedly until all that is left is a patch of black

96.  Shovel loose material onto raised end of riffle box, letting flow of water separate silt and pebbles from heavier sand and gold.

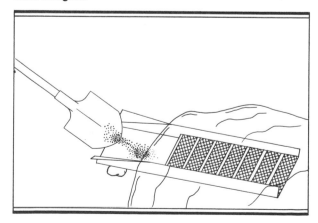

sand and other minerals, perhaps including gold or even a gemstone or two. Add a sip of water, swirl the concentrate across the bottom of the pan and gold, if any, should appear in the tail of the swirl. Pick the gold out with tweezers. Put the rest of the concentrate—usually black magnetic iron sands with small flecks of gold called "flour gold"—in a bottle with concentrates from other pannings. The black sands can be separated from the non-magnetic gold later with a magnet.

Larger amounts of pay dirt can be handled in a sluice or riffle box, which is a trough several feet long, about a foot wide and sometimes half as deep as it is wide (Figure 96). The bottom is covered with carpeting and over that is a quarter inch mesh wire screen, with removable slats or riffles that tend to catch heavy particles and let them fall through to the carpet below. Place the box in the flowing stream and shovel dirt, sand and gravel into the top end. Light dirt and sand is washed away, coarse gravels stay on top, and smaller pieces of gold and other heavy minerals fall through to the carpet below. Later the carpet is lifted out, washed and the concentrate panned for its valuable contents.

Some prospectors use cone screens, which are shaped like a coolie hat. The screen is half filled with dirt, held in the stream coneside down, and lifted up and down under water. The effect is to half float the contents and allow heavy materials to sink into the apex of the cone. Then the cone is removed from the water and quickly inverted so that the heavy material is on top of the pile, where it can be removed and examined.

Where there is little water and brisk breezes, gold can be recovered by tossing the dirt on a blanket so that the light material blows away, a process called winnowing (Figure 13, page 18). On the same principle is the dry washer, a frame on legs topped by a screen that can be shaken, with a platform below. Dirt is shoveled on to the screen; it falls through into a stream of air from a motor-driven bellows that allows only the heavy materials to fall to the platform.

## Triple Screening for Gems

In working gravels for gem crystals, such as the Montana sapphires, good results have been obtained by rigging up three rectangular screens—coarse, medium and fine mesh—one above the other in that order, so that sand can be shoveled from the stream or bank, washed through the screens and the screened material sorted by size. Usually one of the screens will catch most of the crystals.

Some prospectors experienced in the techniques use snorkeling and scuba diving equipment to look for ledges, grooves and cracks in underwater rocks that tend to trap gold like the riffles in a sluice box. Others use dredges—small gasoline engines and water pumps mounted on platforms inside a large inner tube—to suck up sand, water and gravel from stream beds and run it through a riffle box at the surface. Still others use metal detectors to comb not only likely locations of precious metals but also such places as the Michigan copper mine dumps. For more information on the equipment available and how to use it, write for catalogs from the sources listed in Appendix 4.

## Some Collecting Precautions

Most land in the eastern and midwestern United States is privately owned or has been set aside for public use. In the far west vast tracts are under state or federal control. Permission must be obtained to collect on privately-owned land and regulations governing access and collecting on public lands must be observed. According to the 1906 federal Antiquities Act, individuals cannot collect Indian artifacts, vertebrate fossils and other objects defined as antiquities on federal or most state lands. Any collecting is also forbidden in national parks, such as the Petrified Forest National Park in Arizona; national monuments and historic sites, as well as areas under the control of the U.S. Army Corps of Engineers and some areas under the Bureau of Land Management, national forests and some state parks. Regulations in some of these situations change frequently under new concepts of the use of public lands, so inquire before starting a trip to collect.

Trespassing on privately-owned land without obtaining permission is a criminal offense. In some areas the trespasser may even be inviting a shotgun blast from an angry owner, who is not required to put up warning signs. Worse than the illegality of trespass is the bad image it gives the mineral and fossil collecting hobby. To refurbish that image, mineral clubs in some states, notably California, combine a field trip with a cleanup project at some littered camp site or along a bottle-strewn highway.

Common sense and common courtesy dictate other precautions. You shouldn't frighten livestock, trample growing crops, meddle with mine machinery or go beyond the area you have permission to enter. Leave a clean, unlittered campsite with any fire completely extinguished. Leave firearms and explosives at home. Don't go into mines unless you are accompanied by an experienced local miner who knows that it is safe to do so; the multiple hazards and darkness in old mines make them poor choices for prospecting anyhow.

In some areas, snakes, scorpions and ticks are hazards. Always poke into recesses or unexposed areas with a stick before you reach into them. Don't sleep on the ground in the arid southwest; you may wake up to find a snake or scorpion snuggled against you for warmth. Shake out shoes and clothing before dressing and shake out bedrolls at night. If a tick burrows into your skin, make him back out by touching his rump with a hot needle, cigaret, or a dab of turpentine; pulling him out may break off his head which can infect you.

If you are going into strange country, leave word before you depart where you are going and when you expect to be back. Take a companion along. Carry plenty of food, water and fuel so that should you become lost, you can eat, drink and be warm until help comes. Keep calm if you are lost and stay in or near your car; a search party will be along and the car is much easier for searchers to find than you are.

## Collecting Protocol

At the collecting site, use care in climbing over loose rocks, avoid standing on ledges that may crumble, and stay out of deep pits whose walls may collapse. Two collectors digging for emeralds in a deep pit at Hiddenite, N.C. were recently killed when the rain-soaked walls of the pit collapsed on them. Make sure that any rocks you may dislodge do not roll down on collectors working below you.

Considerate collectors never remove any more material than they need personally, picking out only the best and leaving the rest of the material on the spot. Sorting at another locality will only confuse other collectors. Even when one is selective, however, the heavy rocks from a lengthy trip can overload a car's springs, as the authors found out when they returned from gathering agates and geodes in Iowa some years ago. Loaded in the trunk rather than the car body where they could become dangerous missiles in a sudden stop, the heavy rocks pushed the car's nose so high that low beam lights became high beams to oncoming traffic, most of which con-

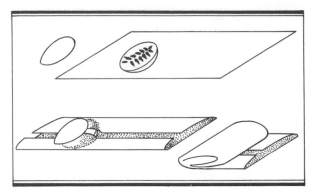

97. To wrap a fossiliferous concretion so that it stays together and is not marred, fold over newspaper and roll as shown above. The same technique can be used to wrap other specimens safely.

sisted of trucks. Since truckers, with their own high beams and spotlights, know how to respond to motorists who don't "dim", the trip back was a slow and painful one.

The solution to such a problem is to ship some material home. Parcel Post and United Parcel Service will take small and delicate specimens, and gunny sacks full of rocks can be shipped by rail as freight at fairly reasonable rates. Wrap each specimen individually (Figure 97), and place delicate crystals in cardboard boxes nested in cotton. Pack small ones in egg cartons, which are light, soft and strong, and place these in a stout cardboard box with crumpled newspaper in the bottom, then add layers of wrapped and packed specimens, separated by crumpled newspapers, so that they will not rub each other. Fill the box full of crumpled newspaper so that the top flaps can be closed only with some difficulty. This will hold the specimens firmly in place. The more weight inside the box the greater the stress on it when it is dropped or roughly handled, so do not overload it. Other good packing materials include the spongy material used for home insulation and plastic pellets.

Bind the box with thread-reinforced paper tape, tie with cord and label legibly. Cover the labeling with Scotch tape. Torn or illegible labels are the most frequent cause of lost packages. If you have wrapped and packed well, the material should arrive home in good condition for the displays or other uses you want to make of it. Some ideas on such uses are given in the chapters that follow.

## Chapter VIII

# Enjoying Your Mineral Treasures

*"Beauty is Nature's coin."*
—Milton

One reason mineral or fossil collecting is fun is that there are no rules to follow. Some collect only minerals, others only fossils. Some specialize in crystals or gems or ores or fluorescents. A collection may be gathered from historic places or from states or countries the collector has visited. Or it may be limited to one kind of rock or fossil. Some collectors try to obtain as many of the 2,500 existing mineral species as they can. Others look only for minerals they can transform into useful and beautiful projects (using the techniques described in Chapter Nine).

Given such a diversity of interests, a desirable specimen is simply one that a collector likes. It enhances his collection—that home mineral museum of which he is the curator. Or it provides new material for his lapidary workshop, of which he is the proprietor. If he found it himself, or obtained it by trading something he had found that another collector needed, the new specimen has a very special value beyond what it may ever be worth monetarily.

Some people buy specimens as a hedge against inflation or in the hope that rarity will make their purchases ever more valuable. As with any investment, this game calls for expert judgment based on a knowledge of minerals, sources, dealers and fashions in collecting. Considering the capricious ways of both Mother Nature and human nature, it is a risky approach for amateur collectors to take.

## Preparing the Specimens

Like a family, a collection needs a home, a feeling of group identity, intelligent care, and an opportunity to be seen under the best circumstances. A specimen from a dealer probably has been carefully trimmed and cleaned, but those brought home from a field trip will need some work before they are ready for display.

Preparation began in the field, where you kept only the most perfect, typical and promising specimens and packed them carefully for the trip home. Use the same care in unwrapping them and wash each one and inspect it for quality and any damage. Then line them up on a table and choose those whose size, beauty or display value will enhance your collection. Here you need to visualize what can be done to improve the looks of specimens that have too much matrix, an awkward shape, or stains and undesirable coatings. Pack up the specimens you have passed over, label them and store them against the time when you may want to trade them with another collector.

Most field specimens need to be trimmed so that the matrix sets off rather than dominates the crystals that are the reason for collecting it. Crusts and stains must also be removed. Soil and clay can usually be removed by spraying the piece lightly with a garden hose, or by soaking it in a bucket filled with soft water and detergent solution. Soak rather than spray if the specimen contains cracks and crystal junctions where hardened clay has lodged. When the clay has softened, it can often be picked out with a sliver of wood or a small steel scraper.

Wash under an outdoor rather than a kitchen or basement faucet, for sand and rock fragments may clog interior drains. Most sturdy rocks and fossils, especially rocks of the quartz family, can be scrubbed with a brush, preferably one made of natural bristles that are less likely than synthetic bristles to scratch the specimen. Don't wash minerals made up of hair-like filaments or very fine needles. Clean them by blowing on them lightly or with a vacuum cleaner hose held far enough away so that its suction won't hurt the specimens. Fossils in shale or other soft rock will disintegrate in water. They must be prepared by use of fine picks, as is done with the Wyoming fossil fish. Or use scrapers to expose and delineate the fossil in its matrix.

## Trimming Specimens

A characteristic matrix is a desirable part of a specimen but it should be kept in proportion to the crystals so that they are not lost in the mass. That is one reason for trimming. Another is to achieve a natural base on which the specimen

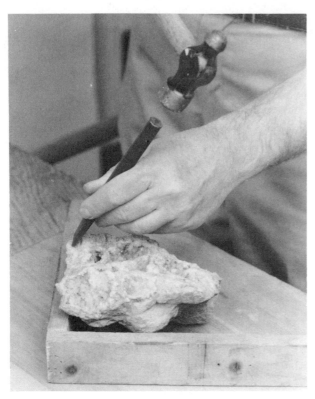

**98. Use a hammer and chisel about the same weight as the specimen and with specimen well braced on a resilient surface, chip away the portions of matrix to be removed. Keep force of blow away from specimen.**

can stand without needing additional support, or with as little such help as possible. Still another reason is that certain sizes of specimens, such as 2-by-4 and 4-by-6 inches, are popular with collectors. If rough specimens can be trimmed to these sizes, they will be more valuable.

Sturdy, non-fragile specimens can often be trimmed with a hammer and chisel that are about the same weight as the specimen. Place the specimen on some shock-absorbing surface, such as a bag of sand or the end of a softwood log, and carefully chip away at the part of the matrix you want to remove (Figure 98). Sometimes there will be strata lines or cracks in the matrix that make it easier to eliminate excess matrix.

More effective trimmers are devices that put screw or hydraulic pressure on two sharpened bits that clamp on the matrix along the line where you want to break it. With such controlled pressure, the rock will part without having the specimen suffer from the shock of hammer blows. Micromounters use small versions of such devices to isolate the tiny crystals they study under high magnification. A substitute for such a press can often be improvised by placing a steel

wedge against the specimen in a bench vise along the line where it is desirable to break it, and then tightening the vise gradually until the specimen parts. This will work only with specimens of favorable shape. For flat and small specimens a strong pair of nippers may be the best trimming tool.

Trimming the matrix of cracked or very fragile specimens is best done with a tungsten-bladed hacksaw or a diamond saw, as described in Chapter Nine (page 141).

## Cleaning Specimens

Remove as many clay pockets and bits of calcite as possible with a toothpick (Figure 99), or by vigorous scrubbing with a toothbrush and pumice or toothpaste if the specimen will stand such treatment. Many advanced collectors and commercial dealers superclean specimens with an ultrasonic cleaner, a tank of water that transmits the tiny shocks of ultrasonic waves to the mineral. While the technique has certain limitations, it does a magnificent job.

Removing disfiguring stains and coatings calls for the use of chemicals. These are strong medicine, so try any chemical treatment first on a poor piece of the same material before using it on a valuable one.

Many crystals, especially those of feldspar, quartz, pyrite and marcasite, are disfigured by rusty iron oxide stains or occasionally black ones of manganese oxides. For iron stains, the preferred reagent is a solution of oxalic acid, a white crystal obtainable at paint or hardware stores. The solution is made of ½ cup of acid to two quarts of warm water. If this solution does not remove the stains, resort to warm hydrochloric acid, usually sold as muriatic acid. When using any acid, remember the AAA rule, *Always Add the Acid* to the water when making a dilute solution. Adding water to acid is very hazardous.

Because it is inexpensive and safer to use than other acids, hydrochloric acid in a 5 to 10 percent solution is preferred for dissolving calcite and other carbonates from specimens, or to improve the appearance of dull crystals of dolomite, calcite and rhodochrosite. A quick dip in the acid suffices; longer immersion will etch the crystals. Many times comparable results can be obtained with acetic acid or vinegar, its household form. Solutions of hydrochloric acid should be discarded when they become yellow from use.

Barite and fluorite specimens can be cleaned in hydrochloric acid. Chemical treatment of any kind, however, should not be overdone, for removal of too much matrix will cause the specimen to fall apart. Sometimes acid can be brushed on part of the specimen to clean it.

Halite (salt) and many of the boron minerals and some sulphates are soluble in water. Marcasite often crumbles in the presence of moisture, and some zeolites deteriorate when exposed to very dry air. Clean these with water-free alcohol and then protect them with a light spray of clear lacquer or rub with mineral oil. One recommended preservative is carpet cement diluted with an equal amount of acetone.

Two troublesome minerals are native silver and copper. Both tarnish in air and lose their metallic beauty. Many home treatments have been devised, including soaking in solutions of drain cleaners, diluted hair wave solutions, and acids. Most acids turn copper an unnatural, bright, ugly pink. The recommended cleaner is a solution of one part by weight of sodium hydroxide (lye), 3 parts of Rochelle salt, and 20 parts of distilled water. The specimen is held by a copper wire and immersed in the solution in a glass or plastic dish.

Silver is easily restored to brightness with one of the thiourea solutions, such as Quik Dip or the cleaner sold in gallon bottles that is used by jewelers and department stores to keep their merchandise sparkling. The silver specimen

**99.** Remove surface dirt by scrubbing with natural bristle brush, using water-free alcohol rather than water on minerals of salt, boron, marcasite or the sulphates. Pick out softened clay pockets with toothpick or a sliver of wood.

should be dipped in the solution, removed at once and rinsed before the chemical has grayed its surface. This solution is more effective for cleaning the so-called halfbreeds of silver and copper in one specimen than the copper cleaner previously mentioned. Silver specimens can be kept bright by wrapping them in the purple cloths supplied by jewelers with purchases of silver flatware, and also used to line flatware boxes for storing silver.

Fossils and some minerals often are stained with tar and oil when taken from a quarry. This coating is readily removed by soaking the specimens in a bucket of unleaded gasoline for a week, then removing and rinsing them in detergent water.

After using any acid or other reagent, you must remove the chemical agent completely from the specimen. Soak the piece for a day or two in tepid water and change the water several times until all trace of the chemical is gone. Porous specimens may require longer soaking. Before spent acid solutions are discarded, neutralize them with pieces of limestone or lime. They can then be poured down the sewer. Make small amounts of chemical solutions harmless by pouring them into several times their bulk of water. Whenever you work with strong acids or alkalis such as lye, wear plastic gloves and safety goggles, and keep baking soda and vinegar close at hand to neutralize splashes of the chemicals on your hands, clothing or equipment.

### Repairing Broken Specimens

Many of the finest specimens in museums have been repaired and are still admired and valued. A clean break, where the edges of the break are not abraded or chipped, is not difficult to repair. Thin epoxy adhesives are excellent for this purpose, as they dry through chemical action rather than evaporation of a solvent, and they can be tinted to match the color of the specimen or left clear. Follow the instructions on the label. Before epoxies were on the market, Canada balsam was the preferred adhesive, and it is still used wherever its optical qualities match those of the crystal. Repaired specimens should be identified as such on their catalog card but not necessarily on the cabinet label.

### Cataloging and Labeling

When a specimen has been washed, trimmed, cleaned and, if need be, repaired, it is time to catalog and label it. The field notes you made while collecting should indicate when and where

**100.  Display specimen of needle hematite, left, is mounted on walnut. Copper sprays, right, are mounted on cork, above, and wood, below.**

the specimen was found, the rock formation it was associated with, and any other details. Locations should ideally identify the exact site by a description—valley, talus pile, or cliff—of the spot and its relation to the nearest village or town, and the county and state. This eliminates ambiguity and confusion. For example, there are Chester and Delaware counties in Pennsylvania, but Chester City is in Delaware County. Plainville and Plainfield are both collecting areas in Connecticut, but more than one careless collector has confused the two names and caused problems for himself and other collectors later.

A specimen purchased from a dealer usually will have a small card with it giving the species and the exact locality by mine, county or province, and country. Insist on getting such a card,

place it in a small glassine envelope and staple the envelope to the back of the catalog card. Similar information should be given and received in a swap of minerals with another collector. Put the name of the dealer or other collector on the catalog card and the date of the transaction, as well as such details as price and history of the specimen, and the previous owners.

The catalog card should, of course, note the location and other information the collector has and how it was obtained, and give a short description of the specimen by size in inches or centimeters (5 centimeters or 2 inches), and its nature, such as group of crystals on matrix, single crystal, polished slab or ore specimen.

Usually the catalog will be arranged by number, what is called an accession catalog, but some collectors also make a second catalog that groups related minerals. This is called a systematic catalog. Catalog entries are most easily typed on 3 x 5 inch cards and kept in a suitable box. If any problems arise about identification, consult a museum curator or an experienced fellow collector.

The relationship between the catalog and the specimen is kept by assigning a number to the specimen that also appears on its catalog card. The easiest way to number the specimen is to paint a small spot on it with white lacquer or nail polish in an inconspicuous place. Let the lacquer dry, then write the number on the spot with India ink and a fine-nibbed pen. The ink, when dry, can be sealed with a dab of colorless lacquer. Some collectors write species, location and catalog number on a tiny piece of paper and glue it to the specimen in an inconspicuous place, (preferably underneath).

A few specimens can be kept in a box partitioned to the size of the pieces, or on a shelf in a china cabinet or bookcase. But display of a collection of any size requires two pieces of furniture—a cabinet in which the specimens can be viewed, and a set of drawers to hold other specimens. Some pieces, of course, can be used for decorative purposes, such as on a fireplace mantel, in a curio table, as accessories in flower and dining table arrangements, shadow boxes and, if they are flat like some sprays of copper, as framed pictures (Figure 45, page 44).

Many collectors have adapted the old-fashioned glass-front china cabinet to the display of minerals and fossils. But these have become fashionable as antiques and are now expensive. Cabinets made especially for mineral and fossil displays are a better value and more convenient. These have hinged or sliding glass doors, glass shelves with ground edges, even

**101.** Mineral display cases with sliding glass doors can be made in sizes that fit the space available.

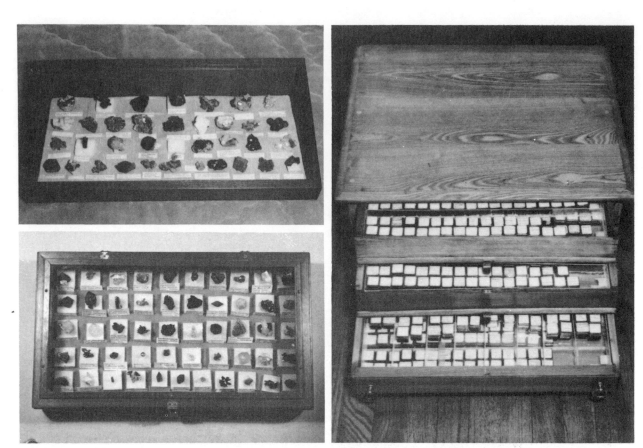

102. Left to right, cabinets are for miniatures (2 inches or less), thumbnails (1 inch or less), and micromounts (tiny crystal specimens). Micromounts are stored in small, individual boxes, each about the size of a quarter.

mirror backs if desired. They are lighted from within, preferably with incandescent bulbs which are more flattering to minerals than fluorescent light (Figure 101). Such cabinets can be mounted on a chest of drawers or can be arranged from floor to ceiling by stacking several sections.

Specimens of thumbnail size—1 inch or smaller—and miniatures—2 inches or less—display their fine crystallizations better in small cases that can be placed on a stand, table or the top of a bookcase (Figure 102). Thumbnails and miniatures are two classes that have been standardized for formal display and competition at mineral shows. They are judged separately from cabinet-size specimens.

Drawers to protect specimens from light, dust and rough handling can be purchased from mineral supply companies or improvised from unfinished furniture, old dental cabinets occasionally available at dental supply companies, and draftsman's cases that may be found at a used office supply firm. Secondhand stores may turn up other pieces of furniture of this sort. A collec-

tor skilled in wood working can make the sort of cabinet exactly suited to his space and collection (Figure 103).

Nature does not always provide display specimens with flat bases that will hold them up to admiration in the cabinet. Sometimes an awkward shape can be improved by sawing the matrix to create a flat bottom for the piece. If this is not possible, the specimen can be mounted on a piece of Styrofoam or a base of polished Lucite with a water-soluble glue such as Elmer's. When necessary, the base can be removed later by soaking the specimen in water. Other ideas for bases to fit various shapes and sizes of specimens are shown in Figures 100 and 104, and in the color section on page 119.

Some collectors place a label typed on a small card in front of each specimen; others let the specimens speak for themselves. Either course has its advantages, but a cabinet is most pleasing to the eye if labels and bases are kept as inconspicuous as possible and if the cabinet is not crowded. Large specimens belong in back where they can be seen without hiding smaller

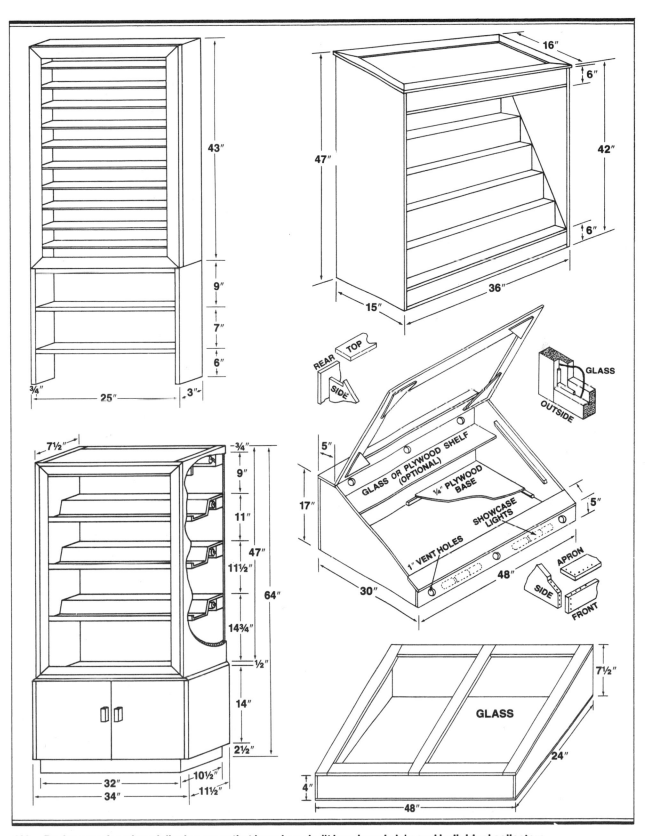

103. Designs are for mineral display cases that have been built by mineral clubs and individual collectors.

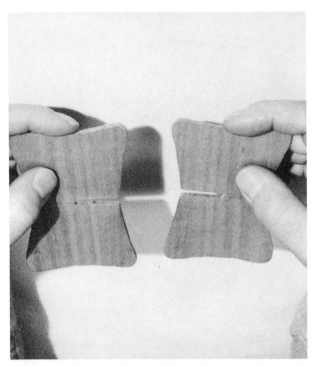

104. Versatile stand for mineral specimens can be made by sawing two identical shapes of wood of the same thickness, then sawing slot the thickness of the wood to the center of each piece. Slip slots over each other and the remaining wood to form the stand (the petrified wood, page 119, is resting on such a stand). Cylinders of mailing tube, plastic or copper pipe also make good stands.

specimens. Some diversity of size, shape and color keeps the collection interesting. Any display should be cleaned and rearranged periodically to make room for new specimens and preserve its freshness.

## Enhancing Collections

Few of us have the time or money to roam the world in quest of new specimens. If a collection is designed to represent minerals and fossils as general groups, it should be enlarged and strengthened by purchase of specimens or trading for new ones. A few generations ago only rich people could do this but now the earth science hobbies are served by a growing industry of dealers in minerals, fossils and gems, and manufacturers of display equipment, lapidary equipment, materials and supplies. There are also books, magazines and collecting guides, and clubs and federations that have shows where collectors can buy, trade with one another, show their treasures competitively or just for fun, meet friends, make new friends and learn what's new in the collecting and craft hobbies.

More than 1,000 clubs interested in collecting, gem cutting and jewelry crafts are active in the United States and Canada, and most hold annual shows open to the public. Many of these clubs are grouped into state and provincial associations, and six regional federations in the United States and several in Canada. These larger groups hold annual conventions and exhibitions; Detroit, Washington, D.C., and Tucson are the scenes of other major shows, and an annual gathering of rockhounds in campers and trailers is a unique affair at Quartzsite, Arizona. These shows bring together hundreds of dealers and equipment manufacturers and thousands of hobbyists. Several Canadian provinces have similar shows, notably at Winnepeg and Toronto.

All this activity is listed and described in the *Lapidary Journal*'s annual April issue Buyer's Guide, along with advertisements of the varied wares of dealers.

As the field has become more highly organized, prices of specimens tend to become standardized, as well as higher. But no two specimens can ever be precisely alike, so prices will vary and it is often possible to get a bargain by shopping around among dealers at shows. Most established dealers are well informed about their specimens and will have them well displayed and labeled. They are also usually eager to help a beginner with advice. Many of them will buy or trade with a collector who has desirable duplicates of minerals and fossils.

## Swapping

Buying is not the only way to supplement what you have collected in the field. Fine collections have been built up by persons with the canniness of a Yankee horse trader and the energy to carry on an active exchange in person and by mail. Such a person can obtain far more value in this way than by selling for dollars. But he can only do so if he knows something about minerals, their real and vogue value, and has something good to swap. At most of the shows mentioned above the swapper will find areas where like-minded collectors are gathered. The usual practice is to designate a swap or trading section in or near the show where traders set up tables on which they can display their treasures. There they will sit as other traders inspect the tables and stop to propose a deal. Sales for money are discouraged in such areas. Specimens shown in a swapping area should be clean, well trimmed and well labeled, and it is wise to have a few especially good specimens held in reserve for the moment when an exceptionally desirable deal comes along. At many informal shows, swapping will be done from tables set up beside a camper vehicle. The collector will find that often swapping is the only means by which he can get specimens peculiar to the area of the show, as many professional dealers will bring only material that they think the local residents do not already have.

## Mail Trades

Specimens are also exchanged by mail. A person wishing to initiate an exchange should indicate his interest by letter to another collector. If the reply is favorable, he should then send properly labeled, clean, good quality specimens, along with some indication of his own special interests. In exchange he should get something of substantially equal value or desirability. In exchanging with or selling to a dealer, material should be priced at a figure low enough so that the dealer can expect to make a profit on its subsequent sale. In exchanging with a beginner, it is good practice to encourage him by your generosity.

Realistic valuation of specimens is the crucial problem in trading. A collector tends to remember the effort he put into a successful field trip and values his specimens accordingly. This can lead to unrealistic expectations in exchanges. Confusion about the identity of a mineral specimen can also cause disputes and hard feelings.

The best insurance here is a carefully kept record of what the specimen is and where it was found. If you are not sure of its identity, consult a museum or knowledgeable collector. They may help you to make a realistic evaluation of what the specimen is worth. Studying what is offered at shows and by mineral dealers in the pages of mineral publications will also give you some idea of the specimen's real value.

## Chapter IX

# Crafting with Minerals and Gems

*"All nature is but art."*
—Alexander Pope

Beautiful, durable rocks have an irresistible appeal to craftsmen, as some of the illustrations in the color sections and in this chapter show. Saw a rock in two and it becomes an attractive pair of bookends (page 119). Cut it into a rectangular block or cube and it can then be shaped into an egg, a sphere, or if it is clear quartz, a crystal ball. With special tools and skills, a chunk of mineral can even be made into a vase or into carved figures like those on pages 116 and 117.

Saw flat slices from the rock and they can be used for clock faces, or as bases for penholders,

lamps, ashtrays, or any scenic display the imagination can concoct (page 119 and Figure 105). Translucent slices can be used for a lamp finial, for window decorations, or to make dramatic wall dividers (page 120). J. L. Kraft, the founder of Kraft Foods, used slices of jade to make a 'stained glass' window for his church in Chicago. Opaque slices with strong colors and patterns can be assembled to make table tops that are conversation pieces (page 120).

From mineral slices—called slabs or flats—gemstones for rings, pendants, bracelets, tie

**105.** Polished flat slices of minerals can be used for bases for desk pens, left, small carvings like these elephants mounted on petrified wood, or, if translucent, dramatic finials for lamps.

baroque gemstones, or perhaps to make a lamp like the one shown on page 120. If you have a transparent crystal, cutting a sequence of flat faces at various angles around the stone will make it refract light like the gemstones on page 77. This technique is called faceting.

Few stones look like gems when you find them, of course. It is the lapidary techniques of first shaping and then polishing that bring out a stone's color and patterns or its jewel-like radiance. You shape the stone by sawing or grinding it. You polish it by sanding and buffing it with successively finer abrasives until the surfaces glisten like glass.

The same basic steps apply whether one is making a pair of bookends or a ringstone. Sawing is done with blades that are smooth metal discs; diamond fragments embedded in their rims do the cutting (Figure 106). Grinding, sanding and polishing are done by working stones against rotating abrasive wheels (Figure 107), or by rotating and vibrating them in a small barrel with a mixture of water and abrasives—the process called tumbling. All work is done wet for lubrication, and to keep frictional heat from cracking the stones.

Sawing a large chunk of rock for, say, bookends or a clock face is best done on a slab saw, which uses diamond saw blades of from 14 to 20 inches or more in diameter. The rock, held in a moveable vise, is fed into the blade at a controlled rate by a hand screw, power feed or

106. Stone held in clamp is moved into spinning diamond saw blade slowly to cut off a slice.

tacs, earrings and other jewelry are cut, as they were for most of the jewelry shown on page 78. Irregularly shaped small stones and pieces left over from cutting larger stones can be ground and polished in a tumbling machine to produce

107. Shaping a gem mineral by turning against a wetted grinding wheel. Work rest on this unit tilts so the edge of stone can be beveled evenly, right.

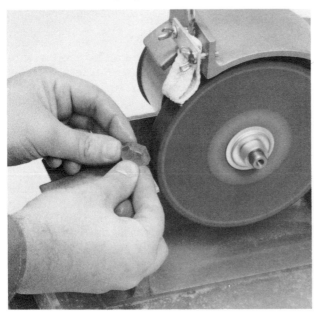

**108. Interchangeable blades, wheels and polishing discs make it possible to cut, shape and polish cabochon gems on this one unit.**

weight mechanism. A commercial light cutting oil or mixture of two parts white kerosene to one part machine oil lubricates the work.

Smaller pieces of mineral can be cut on a trim saw with 6-to 10-inch blades, with water as the lubricant covering about ½ inch of the blade. The mineral is hand fed into the power-driven blade as in Figure 106. (You can also saw minerals by hand, using a special tungsten carbide blade in a regular hacksaw frame. But this is slow, hard work, even for such soft minerals as marble, rhodochrosite or azurite.)

### Slab and Trim Saws

Professionals and advanced amateurs use slab saws but most beginners settle for a trim saw for small work, and either buy preformed rocks or slabs for larger projects, or pay to have them cut and sometimes polished. Rocks and minerals can be purchased in various sizes and shapes from rock dealers or mineral supply houses (Appendix 4). Or local schools, mineral clubs or mineral dealers may have facilities for sawing larger rocks for you.

An ideal arrangement for apartment dwellers who fashion gemstones is a small multipurpose unit whose interchangeable blades and wheels can be used for sawing, grinding, sanding and polishing (Figure 108). With a companion unit, Figure 110, you can also facet gemstones and grind and polish small flats. Larger projects will require larger blades and larger grinding and polishing wheels. Before buying any equipment, however, talk to local mineral club members and dealers and find out what they use for various types of lapidary work and why they prefer it. It is also wise to study the excellent texts on lapidary work listed in Appendix 4; your local library or bookstore may have them.

### Sawing Minerals

Sawing, grinding and polishing are wet, messy procedures. Wear a shop apron and safety goggles for any of this work; mineral chips may fly off, particularly during grinding. For sawing, fix the rock firmly in the vise clamp so that its edge is at right angles to the saw blade (Figure 106). If the edge is irregular, first saw a small notch at right angles to it, then realign rock in the vise so the blade will follow a straight saw cut line without bending or binding. Use small wood shims to help hold irregularly shaped rocks in the vise.

Feed the rock into the blade no faster than ¼ inch a minute for hard minerals like agate and quartz, ½ inch a minute for soft minerals like marble and serpentine. Ease the pressure when the cut is almost through to avoid splintering a piece off the back edge. If the saw blade glazes or clogs, hold a piece of brick against it briefly to clear the cutting surface.

### Grinding Flat Surfaces

Grinding and polishing flat mineral surfaces is called lapping. It is the process you use to finish sawed slabs for desk penholders, window displays, clock faces, inlaid tables and panels, flat gemstones, or the exposed sides of bookends. Small pieces may be lapped on a unit similar to that shown in Figure 110; larger pieces for, say, a pair of bookends are lapped on a larger rotating or vibrating lap (Figure 111).

To grind flat surfaces, silicon carbide abrasives are mixed with water to a thin, non-pasty consistency, then spread across the metal lap wheel. With a vibrating lap, the minerals rest on the wheel and the vibrations do the work. With a rotating lap, the mineral is moved slowly across the face of the wheel while the operator applies light, steady pressure. If the slurry rides up over the mineral, hold it so a very slight curve is formed on one bottom edge; this will let the

109. Imagination is the best designer of mineral projects, as these examples show. Here, reading clockwise from the left are: A lamp made of three wood scraps and copper pipe on which the mineral displayed can be changed each week; a frog carved from purple lepidolite from Maine resting on a base of green serpentine from New Mexico; a carved soapstone bird with dramatically simple lines mounted on variegated marble; a gull from a novelty store sitting on a rough prehnite specimen looking at a small sea shell with interest; and sheets of mica fastened to wire to simulate a modern plant arrangement.

**110.** You can facet gemstones and sand and polish small flats on this unit. A variety of metal dopsticks and a dopstick transfer unit and dopping waxes are in the foreground at left.

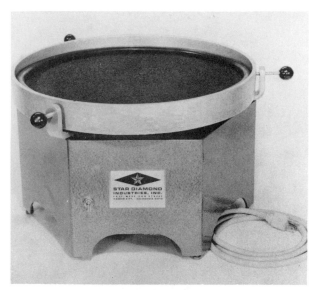

**111.** Lap wheels for larger specimens grind and polish by rotating or vibrating.

abrasive get underneath. A small wood or stone block, attached to the mineral with dopping wax (page 147), will make thin slabs much easier to control.

Some craftsmen lap with only two stages of grinding: 220- and 600-grit silicon carbide. Finer work will result if you use a 220-400-, 600-grit sequence. The mineral, the lap wheel, and your hands and fingernails must all be scrubbed completely clean with hot water and detergent between each grinding stage. Keeping each grit premixed with water in a separate plastic squeeze bottle minimizes grit contamination and makes it easier to spread the mixture across the wheel. But shake the bottles well before using.

Continue grinding until all scratches are gone. Test the evenness of the work by cross hatching it with a pencil; the next grinding should remove all of the lines. When the surface is lightly and evenly frosted all over, scrub it once more and then polish.

### Polishing Flat Surfaces

Use the cloth, felt or leather covered wheel, or the fine abrasive disc that comes with your unit,

for polishing. For cloth, felt or leather-covered wheels, mix a fairly thin slurry of water and polishing agent, and use the slab to spread the mixture evenly over the wheel. Hold slab firmly against the rotating wheel or disc but don't press so hard that you make the stone hot enough to crack it. Rotate the mineral occasionally so that all areas will be evenly polished. Clean off the mineral from time to time and when its surface gleam satisfies you, give it a final scrubbing and

**112.** Adding abrasive mix to one of the newer tumblers which rotate and vibrate at the same time, letting you tumble a batch of stones in seven or eight days.

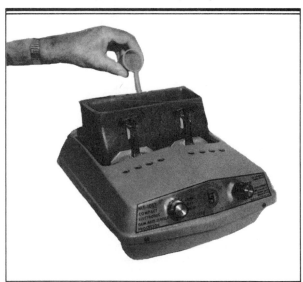

113.  Of various shapes of cabochons, the most popular are the oval or round. Indentations in hearts or where crosses intersect are cut with edge of abrasive stone.

decide how you want to use it. For projects that use polished flats, see Figure 132 and page 156.

### Tumbling Stones

Tumbling is a labor-saving way to polish gemstones but it used to take a month or more.

New tumblers that rotate and vibrate the minerals at the same time now make it possible to tumble a batch of stones in seven or eight days (Figure 112). The tumbled stones retain their irregular shapes but are 10 to 15 percent smaller in size, and have rounded edges and, of course, a polish.

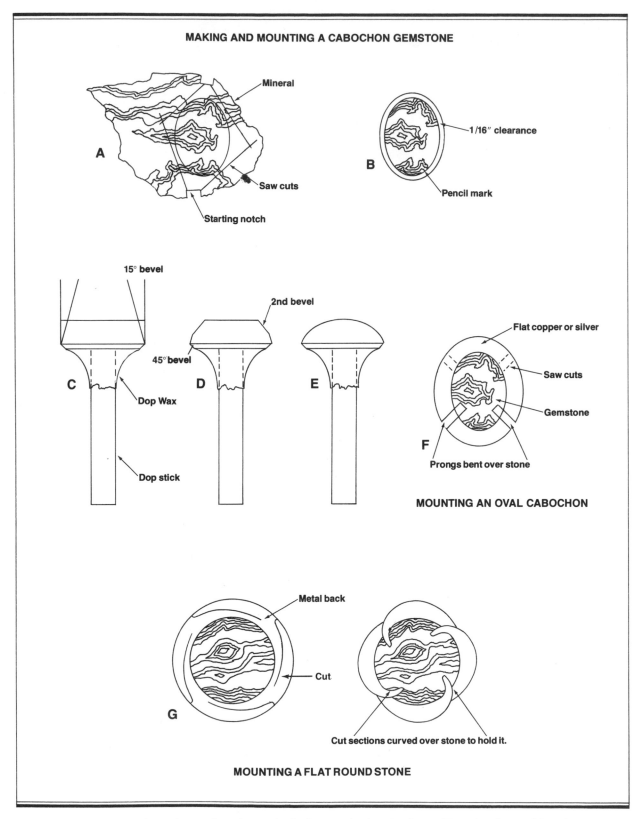

**114.** Steps *a* through *e* show stages of sawing and grinding a cabochon to shape. Steps *f* and *g* are ideas for mounting cabochons and other shapes.

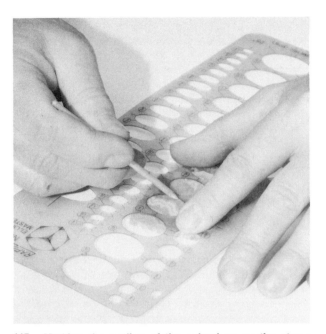

**115.** Marking the outline of the cabochon on the stone using an aluminum pencil or rod. Sharpened tip should touch bottom edge of template all around.

**116.** With mineral clamped firmly saw along lines that enclose the cabochon as indicated in Figure 114a.

Select stones of about equal hardness that have no deep pits or cracks. Follow the instructions that come with the tumbler for the weight and type of load, the proportions of water and abrasive mix to use, and the length of time for each tumbling phase. The instructions may call for a day or two of coarse and then fine grinding, first with 80- and then 220-grit abrasives, followed by a prepolish with finer abrasive and a final polish with a polishing compound such as aluminum oxide and water. Separate barrels or liners (or scrupulously cleaned barrels) must be

**117.** To fasten stone to wood or metal dopstick, heat stones on top of tin can stove with alcohol lamp as at left. Then melt dop wax until a blob can be pulled off on top of wood dopstick, or until it flows into end of metal dopstick, as at right, and press stone into hot wax. Wood dopsticks can be held by hand; the metal dop in its transfer unit shown here is for dopping and transferring faceted stones.

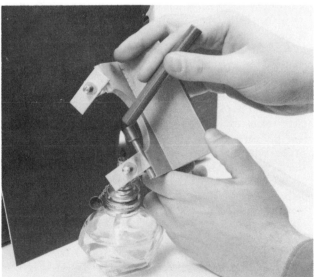

**118. Use one hand to brace and the other to turn the dopstick as you grind the bevel around the stone.**

used with each grit to keep from contaminating finer grits or polishes with rough grits.

For projects that use tumbled stones in jewelry or in a mineral lamp see Figure 133 and page 157.

### Making Cabochon Gemstones

A cabochon is an unfaceted gemstone, usually oval or round in outline with a domed top (Figure 113). It is cut from a slab or flat piece of mineral whose thickness determines the height of the dome. The steps in making a cabochon are shown in Figure 114. You will need a plastic template with pattern cutouts, a pointed bronze or aluminum rod or pencil, a 4-inch long dowel called a dopstick (c in Figure 114), dopping wax to fix the stone to the dopstick, an alcohol lamp to melt the wax, and a tall tin can or dopping stove for heating the stone. Mineral dealers stock these items.

Move the template over the slab until the cabochon outline you want encloses an interesting pattern. Make sure the corresponding area underneath the mineral has about the same pattern, since that will be the dome of your cabochon; you mark the base. Draw the cabochon outline (Figure 115). Then draw straight lines for saw cuts that come to within about ⅛ inch of the outline (a in Figure 114). Make these cuts as in Figure 116.

Grind in toward the cabochon outline on a 100-grit silicon carbide grinding wheel (Figure 107) with water adjusted to come off the moving wheel in a fine, misty spray. With hands well braced, hold stone firmly and sweep it across the front of the wheel in an arc that parallels the curved edge of the cabochon. Work off any sharp points by grinding toward them, first from one side, then the other.

Keep the edge of the stone at right angles to its top and bottom faces. When you have ground to within 1/16-inch of the pencil mark all around (b in Figure 114), scrub the stone clean in warm water and detergent and change over to a 220-grit wheel.

Grind a small 45-degree bevel around the base of the cabochon (c in Figure 114). Let the bevel barely touch but not obliterate the outer edge of the pencil mark.

To shape the cabochon (or to do any grinding on small cabochons) the stone must first be fixed to a dopstick (c in Figure 114). Place the stone on top of a tin can stove (Figure 117) and heat the end of the dopping wax until it softens enough to pull off a small blob onto the end of the dopstick. Press tip of dopstick firmly against the center of the heated stone and shape wax evenly around the dopstick and up against the stone (c in Figure 114). But don't cover up the pencil mark. Use a nail or small tool or dip your fingertips in water to start shaping the wax before it has cooled enough to work comfortably. Make sure the dopstick butting against the stone is perpendicular to the stone.

Grind the two bevels (c and d in Figure 114) with one hand braced against the tool rest to hold the stone at the correct angle, and the other hand moving the stone around the circumference of each bevel (Figure 118). Level out the ridges between bevels and then form the curved dome (e in Figure 114). Use rocking and arcing motions as you rotate the stone. Keep the stone moving, keep the wheel wet and let it do the work. Maintain the 15-degree angle of the first bevel at the base of the stone; it will be needed for mounting the stone (f in Figure 114). Check stone frequently from all sides to make sure the curves being formed are balanced.

When the basic shape of the stone is correct, scrub the cabochon clean in warm water and detergent. Then sand out scratches left from grinding, first on a 400-grit, then, after scrubbing clean, on a 600-grit sanding belt or abrasive disc. Use the same arcing, turning motions as for grinding but keep pressure gentle to avoid changing the stone's shape. Sand until no scratches or small pits are visible after giving the stone a hard scrubbing with water and detergent. Sanding grit caught in such flaws will spoil the polish.

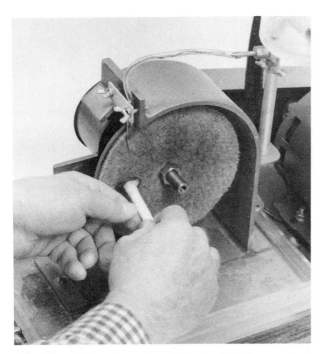

119. To polish, rotate and rock the sanded stone against the polishing wheel that comes with your equipment. Keep wheel wet with slurry and stone moving and turning. When you begin to feel a slight tugging action, ease up on the pressure but polish until the surface shine suits you.

Polish on the polishing wheel that comes with your equipment (Figure 119), using a slurry of water and cerium oxide or other polishing agent. Keep the wheel damp with the slurry and the stone moving and turning. Apply a fair amount of pressure but ease up when you feel a tugging action, which means you are beginning to get a polish. Polish until the appearance of the surface pleases you, then scrub stone clean. To separate the stone from the dopstick, place in ice water for a few seconds; the wax becomes brittle and the stone will pop off with a light tap. If any wax remains, clean off with alcohol and a single-edged razor blade.

The cabochon may be mounted as in Figure 114 f or g. Or you can buy from craft or mineral supply houses a ring, tie tac, pendant or other type of jewelry finding to which the cabochon may be fixed with epoxy cement as were most of the stones on page 78.

## Faceting Gemstones

Faceting crystals so that they will sparkle like a diamond ring sounds difficult but many amateurs are doing it today. Versatile new equipment and easy-to-follow instructions have taken most of the toil and trouble out of faceting.

The basic idea is to cut flat faces (facets) in a crystal at angles that bounce light entering the stone from facet to facet until it emerges through the top or crown of the stone (Figure 120). If the wrong angles are used, light leaks out through the bottom or pavilion of the stone and you can see through the stone; lapidaries call this a "fish eye." If the right angles are used, much of the light is returned through the crown as sparkle.

The cutting angles are determined by the refractive index of the mineral being cut, and books on lapidary work (Appendix 4) specify the angles that will provide the greatest brilliance or sparkle for different minerals, as well as for the style of cut. The standard brilliant cut (Figure 59, page 68) is the most popular style.

The crystal selected for faceting should be as free of flaws as possible, particularly in the area that will be readily visible through the table of the finished stone. Except in rare cases where the natural crystal shape tends to conform to the outline of the finished gem (as garnets do for round brilliant cuts), count on losing about 70 percent of the crystal during cutting and polishing. That is why it is wise to start faceting with a mineral like quartz, which is easier to work and costs much less than the harder rubies, sapphires and diamonds.

While it is impossible to provide a complete course on faceting in one brief chapter, Figures 121 through 131 are a good introduction to the art. They show major steps involved in faceting, as demonstrated by craftsman Gerry Pietrafesa Jr. Some results of his work are shown on page

120. When facets are cut at the correct angle for the mineral used and the style of cut, light entering the stone will bounce from facet to facet until it emerges through the top of the stone.

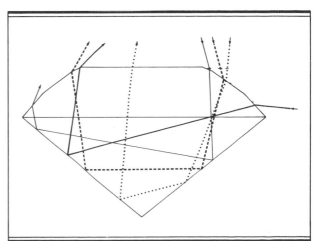

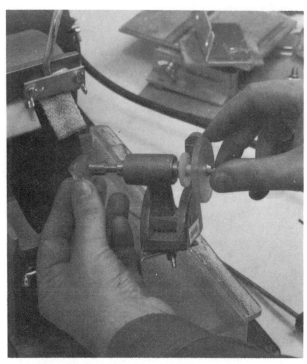

121. Before faceting a brilliant cut, the crystal is beveled to preform shape, using an attachment that holds the stone at a 45-degree angle to the face of the grinding wheel.

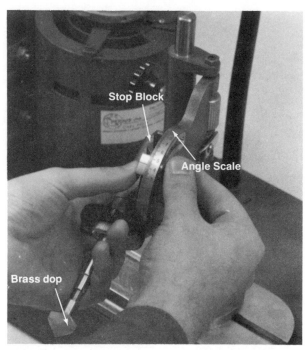

122. With stone fixed to brass dop and dop mounted in the faceting spindle, set the angle for cutting the main pavilion or bottom facets by aligning the mark on the stop block with angle scale on the faceting spindle of this Graves unit.

123. Left thumb releases latch lever so that index plate can be set for cutting eight equidistant main pavilion facets. The settings to use are given in texts on faceting techniques.

124. With water turned on to release 12 drops a minute onto 180-grit lap wheel, mast is raised to its highest point to clear splash pan, then rocked down until the stone barely touches the 180-grit lap wheel. Lock mast screw and use micrometer adjustment to lower stone until it touches wet moving wheel firmly when swept back and forth across it.

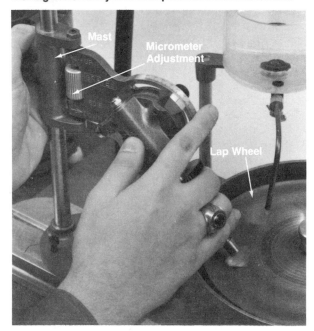

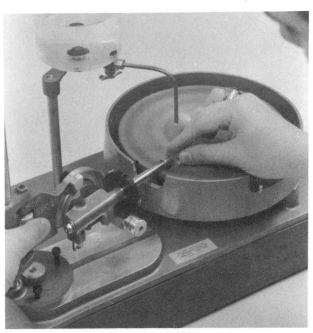

125. Continue sweeping until stone travels across lap without making a sound. Repeat the procedure with 600-grit wheel substituted for 180-grit wheel. Set index plate for next main pavilion facet and continue until all these facets are cut. Then change angle and index settings to cut break facets in pavilion, using settings specified in texts.

126. Cut girdle facets with spindle readjusted so that it is parallel to the lap wheel surface, with plastic covering opening in splash pan removed to provide spindle access. Set angle at 90 degrees and use same index setting as for break facets. Polish main, break and girdle pavilion facets with 1.5 micron cerium oxide plastic disc that comes with unit.

127. After pavilion facets are cut, transfer stone from male to female dop so that top or crown facets may be cut. Melt stick shellac into female dop, press pavilion of stone into shellac until it touches the edge of the dop (left, above), and let cool. Then heat tip of male dop until it drops off the stone (right, below).

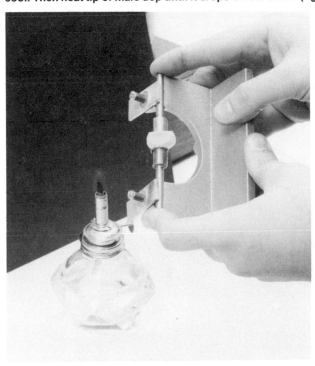

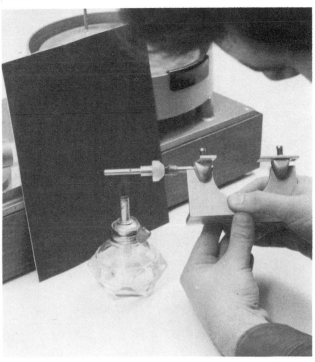

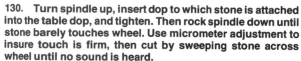

128. Cut and polish crown facets as you did pavilion facets, following the settings specified in texts for the material being cut. But, to cut the flat table of the stone, insert table dop shown here in the spindle, and set index for cutting the table for this type brilliant.

129. Rock table dop down until it is perfectly flat on lap wheel. Then tighten the spindle with the Allen wrench supplied.

130. Turn spindle up, insert dop to which stone is attached into the table dop, and tighten. Then rock spindle down until stone barely touches wheel. Use micrometer adjustment to insure touch is firm, then cut by sweeping stone across wheel until no sound is heard.

131. Final polishing of table is done with 1.5 micron disc substituted for the diamond-impregnated lap wheel.

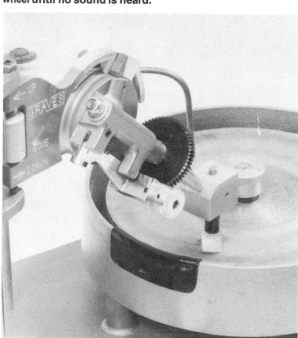

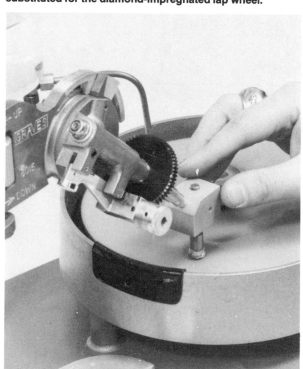

77. If you are interested in learning more about faceting, study the texts in Appendix 4, and find out if local schools or mineral clubs offer courses that let you learn under the guidance of an experienced lapidary.

## Mounting Gemstones

A wide variety of mountings for cabochon and faceted gems can be obtained from mineral dealers or supply houses. If none of these suits you, you can design your own. Figures 114 *f* and *g* show ways to mount oval or round cabochon or flat stones, and the same techniques could be used for square, triangular or rectangular shapes. But what if the shape is irregular? You can make an attractive mounting for it using the technique shown for the brooches in Figure 132.

Lay the stone on a flat piece of 20 gauge copper or silver. Draw a line that follows the stone's outline but is about ⅛ inch outside of it. With the stone still in place, mark four points next to it where prongs would hold it securely. Remove the stone and draw lines for slots from the prong points you have marked diagonally in toward the center of the metal. Make the slots slightly longer than the thickness of the stone, and taper them so that they are 3/32-inch wide at the prong points and narrow down to 1/16-inch wide where the slots end.

**132. For irregular shapes, place stone on metal, draw outline on metal about ⅛-inch outside stone, and cut prongs to hold stone as described in the text.**

**133. Form wire cage around tumbled stones, with loop at the top, to hold them for earrings or pendants.**

Drill a 1/16-inch hole at the end of each slot nearest the center of the metal. Insert a jeweler's saw blade and saw along each side of each slot until you reach the prong point. Push up the pieces of metal freed by the saw cuts to form four small prongs. Place stone within the prongs and bend the prong tips in slightly to hold the stone in place. Cement a pin-back jewelry finding to the back of the metal to complete the brooch.

Mounting irregularly shaped tumbled stones may call for different solutions. If they don't have a flat side or a rounded tip that can be cemented onto or into a jewelry finding, form wire cages around them as in Figure 133. Make a small loop at the top of the cage and attach to a chain or earring findings.

## Gemstone Eggs

For gemstone eggs similar to those shown on page 119, you need a rectangular mineral block roughly the same width and height but ¾ longer. Bevel off all sharp edges of the block by grinding toward them from either side on a 100-grit wheel. Divide the block into three sections (Figure 134). Grind cylindrical bands for the front, rear and middle sections of the egg, then eliminate the ridges between bands by rocking the egg back and forth along its length as you turn it against the grinding wheel. The ends of the egg are then rounded by working toward them with short curved strokes as you rotate the egg. When properly shaped, the egg should roll on a table in a smooth arc without wobbling. Sand and polish

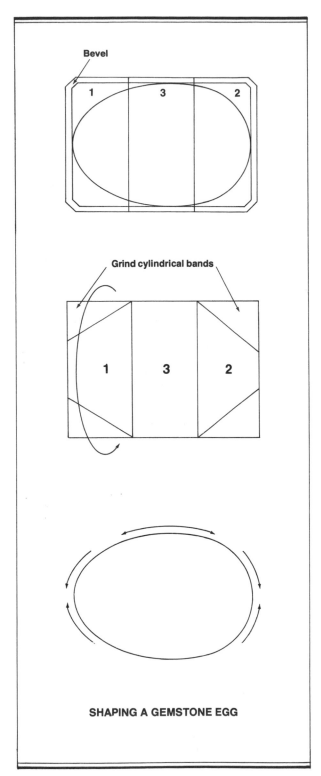

Bevel

Grind cylindrical bands

**SHAPING A GEMSTONE EGG**

134. To form a gemstone egg from a rectangular block of mineral, first bevel all edges. Then divide block into thirds and shape the front and rear bands first, then the middle band. Eliminate ridges between bands by rocking egg back and forth as you turn it. Shape the ends and polish the egg as explained in the text.

the egg following the steps given for finishing cabochons (page 148).

### Making Spheres

Spheres are made from cubes of minerals. Circles are drawn on all sides of the cube and all edges, corners and projections are sawed or ground off to achieve a rough, ball-like contour. To smooth this into a sphere, the ball is held between two sections of cast iron pipe or heavy walled tube, one of which is mounted in a lathe or on a lap wheel spindle (Figure 135). Each pipe's outer diameter should be slightly smaller than the diameter of the finished sphere. A curved bevel filed on the inside lips of the pipes helps them to conform to the shape of the sphere.

Grinding is done at slow speeds—no more than 1750 revolutions per minute for spheres less than 1 inch in diameter, down to about 600 revolutions per minute for spheres 2 to 3 inches in diameter. The end of both pipes are stuffed with wetted, abrasive-loaded cloths, and the ball, coated with a thin abrasive slurry, is held against the end of the pipe as in Figure 135. From time to time, more slurry is applied to the sphere and the pipe rags. The pipe ends become sharper with grinding and should be blunted occasionally with a file so fingers that might accidentally touch them will not be cut. Finer abrasives are used as the sphere becomes smoother. Clean the work and equipment carefully between each change in abrasive.

When the shape seems right and all scratches have been removed, clean the sphere and the pipe, and tightly bind a piece of leather or wetted fine abrasive cloth over the pipe end. If leather, coat with a thin slurry of water and polishing agent. Polish the sphere as you ground it. Small spheres may be mounted on a dopstick and polished as you would a cabochon (Figure 119). After polishing more than half of the sphere, remount it with the unpolished side out, and polish that side and enough more to eliminate any line that might separate the two polishings.

Some mineral dealers stock sphere-making machines and sphere-making caps that fit into lathe chucks or on lap wheel spindles. Or a steel rod that fits into your equipment can be welded to one end of the pipe.

### Window Displays and Wall Panels

Translucent minerals with striking colors or patterns make a fine window display (page 119). Construction of a rack to hold them is shown in

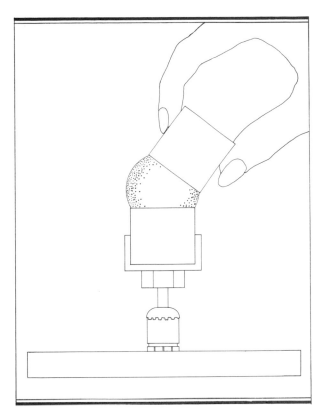

**135.** After a cube of mineral has been sawed to a rough ball-like shape, it is ground into a small sphere between two sections of pipe, each loaded with abrasive, as described in the text.

Figure 136. Or you may prefer to arrange them in a design, cement the pieces to a pane of glass with epoxy, and then frame the glass and place it on the window sill; the cross shown on page 120 was made this way. The same technique, on a larger scale, can be used to make dramatic room dividers (page 120).

## Bases for Pen Holder and Other Projects

Desk pens and swivels may be attached to polished flats, as in Figure 105, using contact cement supplied with the swivel. Larger stationery stores carry these pen and swivel sets (Sheaffer's Deskette is one model). Polished flats also make good bases for scenes with small animals, birds or human figures that can be fixed to the base with epoxy (page 119 and Figure 105); let your imagination do the designing.

Grinding and polishing a concave depression in the middle of a thick flat makes it into an attractive ashtray. This is best done with special ball-shaped or rounded edge grinding wheels, but regular grinding wheels of the right diameter will work if used carefully.

Felt glued to the bottom of polished flats will protect furniture surfaces.

## Inlaid Table Top

Embedding flat slices of minerals in polyester plastic created the round table top on page 120. For a table that size you would need a special form in which to cast the plastic. A top for a small table can be cast in a large cake pan, following the technique shown in Figure 137. After running a thin ribbon of window caulk around the inside seam of the pan and coating the inside with silicone or wax mold-release agent, the plastic is mixed with catalyst and poured in thin layers. When the first layer hardens, minerals are laid on it, and a second layer is poured. Additional thin layers are poured to cover the minerals and complete the table-top casting. Chips of minerals may be mixed with the added layers of plastic as the turquoise chips were for the table on page 120. A dark coloring agent is added to the final layer to hide the legs, since this will be the underside of the table top.

When the final layer has hardened, the pan is turned over and tapped to release the plastic, which is then sanded with very fine abrasive paper and polished with plastic buffing compound on a cloth or flannel buffing wheel. Craft supply stores stock the plastic and other materials you will need. Carefully follow the instructions that come with the casting plastic and be sure to wear gloves and work in a well-ventilated place.

Wood or metal legs for the top can be purchased from hardware or lumber stores. Or you might find that an old banister or newel post will do nicely.

The same technique of embedding minerals in plastic can be used to make small objects such as paperweights. Minerals can also be set in cement rather than plastic, as they were for the rectangular table top shown on page 120. The top is then given several protective coats of acrylic lacquer.

## Mineral Clock

A flat slice of mineral six inches in diameter makes a dramatic battery-powered clock like the one shown in Figure 139 and on page 119. Kits for such clocks include the basic movement and its shaft, the minute, hour and second hands, and the necessary nuts and washers; one kit is sold by General Time.

Mark a center point on the mineral for the clock shaft. From this point draw a circle with a

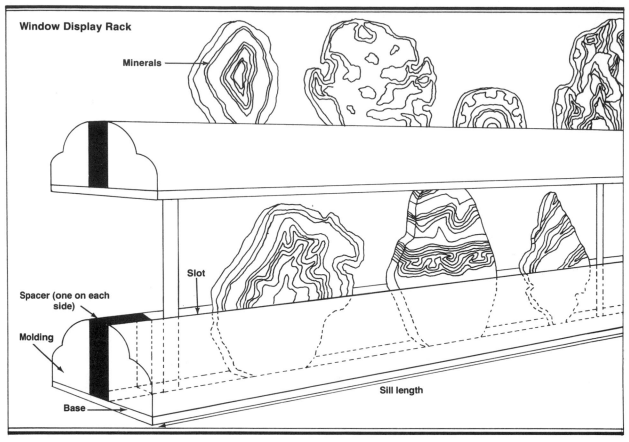

**Window Display Rack**

Minerals

Spacer (one on each side)

Molding

Base

Slot

Sill length

136. Two pieces of molding fastened to a base, with wood spacers keeping them apart, will hold translucent minerals for window display. If you want a double decker, drill holes for dowels in the bases of the top and bottom racks and glue dowels into place. The completed rack is shown on page 119.

137. To embed minerals for a table top, a first layer of polyester plastic is poured, the minerals are placed on it when it gels, and additional layers are poured to complete the table top as described in the text. Pouring plastic slowly down a stick helps keep bubbles from forming in the plastic.

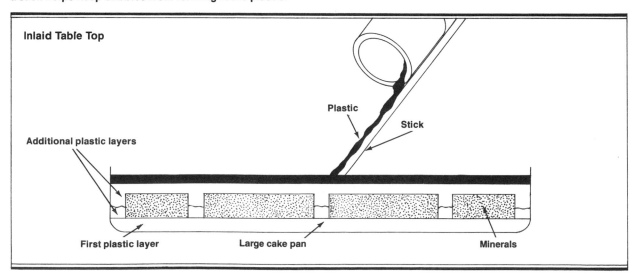

**Inlaid Table Top**

Plastic

Stick

Additional plastic layers

First plastic layer

Large cake pan

Minerals

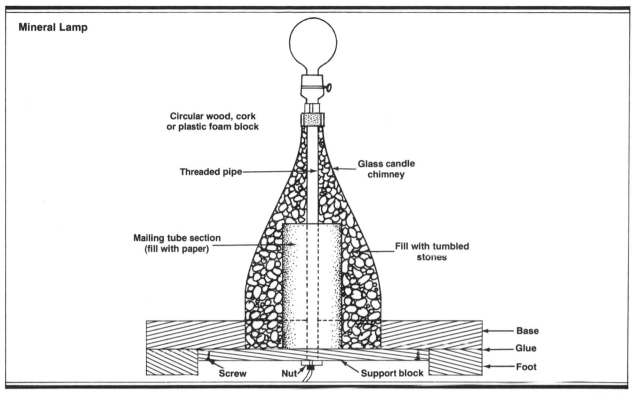

**Mineral Lamp**

Circular wood, cork or plastic foam block

Threaded pipe

Glass candle chimney

Mailing tube section (fill with paper)

Fill with tumbled stones

Base

Glue

Foot

Screw

Nut

Support block

138. This side view of the clock on page 119 shows the simple construction. Information on drilling the hole through the mineral for the clock shaft is given in Figure 140.

139. Cross section view of the lamp on page 120 shows how it is made. Construction steps are explained in the text.

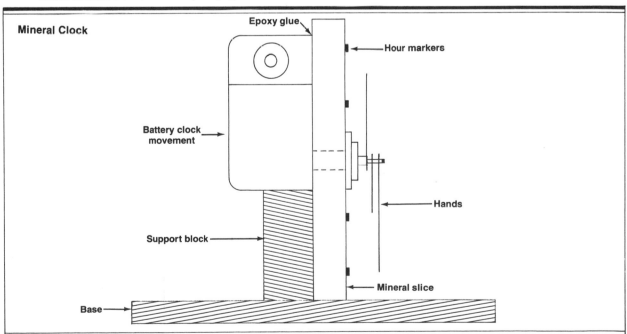

**Mineral Clock**

Epoxy glue

Hour markers

Battery clock movement

Hands

Support block

Mineral slice

Base

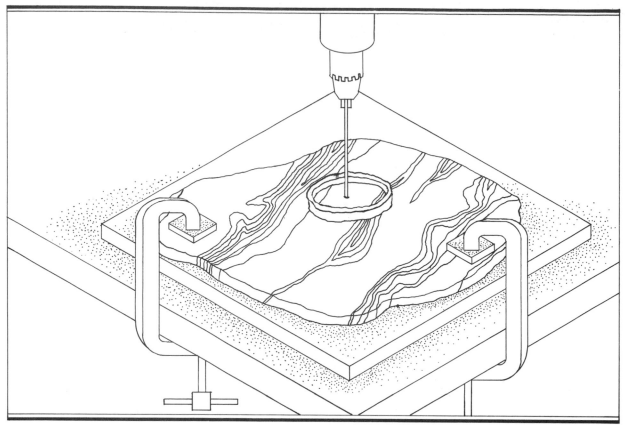

140.   To drill a hole through a flat mineral for a clock shaft, clamp or glue mineral to scrap wood, and form a circular clay dam around the hole to hold the water coolant. Fit a diamond core drill (available from lapidary supply houses) into the chuck of a drill press or stand-mounted electric drill. After lining up drill with hole location, pour water in dam and lower drill to drill hole at about 1500 rpm. Keep pressure light. A 5/16-inch drill was correct for the shaft of the General Time movement used in the clock on page 119.

141.   After mineral has been roughly shaped with larger tools, the carved details are made with smaller grinding and sawing tools, as at left. Some of the different shapes of instruments used for the finer work are shown at right below.

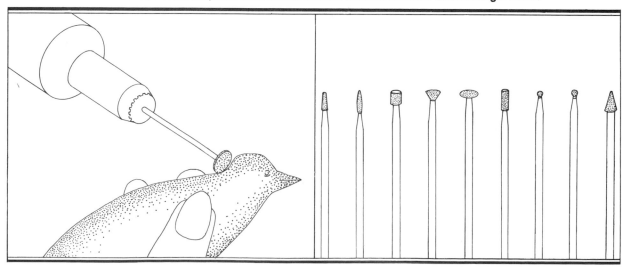

radius ⅛-inch longer than the length of the long minute hand from its tip to the shaft hole. With a protractor or compass mark the 12 hour positions on the circle, each separated by 30 degrees. The hour markers on the clock shown are small circles punched out of a gold Christmas card with a paper punch and glued around the circle at each hour position. But don't attach them until the center hole for the clock shaft has been drilled.

A local mineral dealer should be able to drill the shaft hole for you. Or, if you own or can borrow or rent a drill press or a variable speed power drill with a stand that will lower the drill, make the hole as in Figure 140. Then cut out the base and supporting block, attach the hour markers, and assemble the clock as in Figure 139.

## Mineral Lamp

Construction of a lamp for displaying tumbled gemstones is shown in Figure 138. The body of the lamp is a glass candle chimney from a local hardware store or candle shop. Cut a circular block of wood, cork or plastic foam to fit into the narrow neck of the chimney and drill a hole for the threaded electrical pipe in the center of the circular block. Cut and assemble the parts for the base, drilling a hole for the threaded pipe in the center of the support block; use a saber saw

## Photographing Minerals and Gems

This can be a hobby in itself but good results call for practice and experimentation. In our strictly non-professional experience, a display case of minerals can be photographed with almost any kind of camera if the case is adequately lighted and the film used is adjusted for color sensitivity to the lighting used. Bounce lighting your flash or using indirectly aimed photofloods will eliminate hot spot reflections from the glass in the case or the crystal surfaces of the specimens.

Photographing individual specimens calls for cameras and lenses that let you take closeups. We've had good luck with a Nikormat 35-mm through-the-lens camera (to avoid parallax problems), with a Micro-Nikor lens which permits focusing up to 7 inches from the specimen. Other camera makers have similar equipment. You'll have to experiment with light placement, reflector screens and back lighting that emphasizes crystal structure, and a study of the professional photographs in the color sections of this book should provide useful clues. It's always wise to take three shots of each specimen—one at the indicated exposure, one at an "f" stop above and one at an "f" stop below.

## Photographing fluorescents

This is a tricky art that calls for a filter to keep the ultraviolet light from overexposing the film. Here are some guidelines from the experts at Ultraviolet Products, Inc. Use a Wratten 2A filter or a 2B type if 2A is not available. Try Kodachrome Type 2 Daylight film with an ASA index of 50. With two large short-wave ultraviolet lights 18 inches away from the specimen, a Wratten 2A filter, Kodachrome 2 film and an "f" stop at 16, good photos resulted with exposures of about 48 seconds. With two small short-wave lamps placed 6 or 8 inches from the specimen, exposure time was increased as much as four times to get good results. Remember that the distance of the specimen from the light source (not its distance from the camera) is what's important. So is the power of the light source; the more powerful it is, the shorter the exposure needed.

Specimens that fluoresce red and green, like those from Franklin, New Jersey, shown on page 113, require a shorter exposure than those that fluoresce blue, such as scheelite, which may require twice as much exposure time.

Long-wave ultraviolet lights transmit more deep violet visible light than short-wave lights do. This reflects back from the mineral and can distort its true fluorescent colors. To eliminate the reflection on those minerals that fluoresce orange, yellow or green, try a yellow filter such as the K2.

As a final rule of thumb, remember that it's often better to use smaller "f" stops and a longer time exposure to avoid errors due to inaccuracy of time measurement.

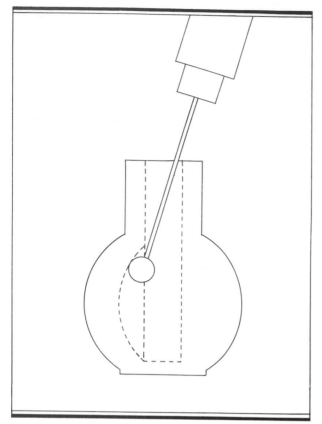

**142.** To hollow out the inside of a vase, a hole is first drilled straight down the center and then the hole is widened with ball-shaped grinding tools inserted through the vase neck at various angles.

to cut a circle in the base into which the wide end of the chimney will fit. Cut the threaded pipe to length with a hacksaw, insert it through the hole in the block and fix washers and nuts to the top of the pipe. With the block and pipe in place, upend the chimney and load stones into the neck of the lamp from the bottom.

The section of cardboard mailing tube shown helps to fill space in the lamp so you won't need as many stones. When you have enough stones in the upended neck to support the mailing tube, slip it over the pipe and stuff the tube with tissue to fill the empty space between the tube and the pipe. Continue filling the chimney around the tube with stones until the chimney is full. Then fit the base over the chimney so the bottom of the pipe comes through the hole made for it in the supporting block. Attach washer and nut to fix pipe against the supporting block and turn lamp upright on its base. Attach lamp wire to socket terminals, thread wire down through pipe until you can screw socket base to top end of pipe, and tighten the socket screw to hold it. Then attach wall plug to the other end of the wire and your lamp is complete.

## Carving, Sculpturing and Engraving Minerals

These advanced techniques call for considerable artistry, and manual dexterity. But the basic procedures use many of the techniques previously

**143.** To make a flat mineral into an ashtray, you can grind a concave depression with the curved edge of a regular grinding wheel (A), or by using a ball-shaped grinder (B). If a lot of material must be removed, grind a circular groove around the top to define the concave area. Then criss-cross the area with the edge of a diamond saw blade (C), break out the pieces between slices, grind the concave area smooth and then polish.

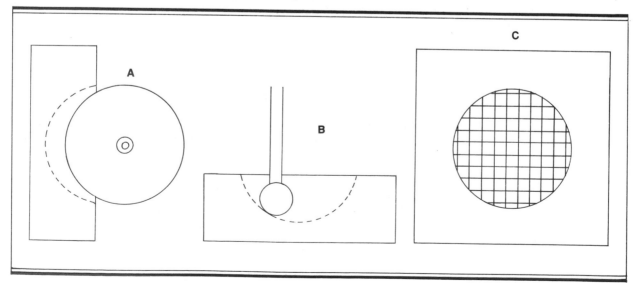

described. The minerals are first sawed and ground to the rough shape desired. A template of the final design is made and the work is checked against the template at frequent intervals. For small intaglio engravings, the stone can be coated with a light-colored lacquer, on which the design is traced when the lacquer has dried. The design is then traced with a diamond stylus.

Carvings are roughly blocked out with ball-, oval- and cylindrically-shaped diamond tools and small saws. Finer details are then carved with smaller grinding and cutting tools of various shapes (Figure 141). Small saw blades, for example, are used to cut fine lines in the carving. Holes are made using the correct sized drill and the technique described in Figure 140. To hollow out the inside of a vase, a central hole is first drilled through the neck of the vase toward the bottom. Small ball-shaped tools are then inserted in the drilled hole and used to widen or hollow out the interior (Figure 142). The inside of bowls and cups are hollowed out using the technique shown in Figure 143 (C).

Sanding and polishing are done with small wheels covered with fine abrasive cloth and leather, muslin, felt and fine abrasive and polishing compounds. All carving work requires a delicate touch and undivided attention to keep from jamming the tool into the outlines of the carving and breaking or marring the work. If you are interested in trying carving, study some of the excellent lapidary books listed in Appendix 4. Then develop a simple design and try it out on some soft, easily carved mineral like gypsum, fluorite, azurite or marble. You may be surprised to discover how talented you are.

The foregoing projects are only a small sample of what beginners can make with rocks and minerals, using various lapidary techniques. Perhaps the sample—and the minerals you work with—will stimulate you to develop original designs of your own. With their infinite variety of patterns and color combinations, minerals do have a way of telling craftsmen what can best be done with them, and their beauty inspires craftsmen to accept the challenge.

# Commoner Chemical Elements

| | | | | | |
|---|---|---|---|---|---|
| Aluminum | Al | Hydrogen | H | Radium | Ra |
| Antimony | Sb | Iodine | I | Selenium | Se |
| Arsenic | As | Iridium | Ir | Silicon | Si |
| Barium | Ba | Iron | Fe | Silver | Ag |
| Beryllium | Be | Lead | Pb | Sodium | Na |
| Bismuth | Bi | Lithium | Li | Strontium | Sr |
| Boron | B | Magnesium | Mg | Sulfur | S |
| Bromine | Br | Manganese | Mn | Tantalum | Ta |
| Cadmium | Cd | Mercury | Hg | Tellurium | Te |
| Calcium | Ca | Molybdenum | Mo | Thorium | Th |
| Carbon | C | Nickel | Ni | Tin | Sn |
| Cerium | Ce | *Niobium | Nb | Titanium | Ti |
| Chlorine | Cl | Nitrogen | N | Tungsten | W |
| Chromium | Cr | Oxygen | O | Uranium | U |
| Cobalt | Co | Phosphorus | P | Vanadium | V |
| Copper | Cu | Platinum | Pt | Zinc | Zn |
| Fluorine | F | Plutonium | Pu | Zirconium | Zr |
| Gold | Au | Potassium | K | | |

*Formerly named columbium.

---

Stable minerals are made up of a positively-charged element or group of elements, which is written first in the mineral formula, and a negatively-charged element or group, which is written after the first one. For example, positively-charged sodium (Na) and negatively-charged chlorine (Cl), form NaCl, sodium chloride, common salt.

The positively charged members are usually a metal or group of metals, such as Fe (iron) or FeMn, (iron-manganese), which may exist in varying proportions and is usually written (Fe,Mn) to indicate that one or both may be present. Such a variation in composition is common among some minerals. A positive metal or group combines with a negatively-charged one such as the sulphur (S) of the sulphides like covellite, CuS, which are usually heavy and have metallic luster; the oxygen (O) of the oxides, like zincite, $ZnO$; the hydroxyl (OH) of the hydroxides like NaOH, which is lye; the chlorine (Cl) of the chlorides such as salt, NaCl; and the fluorine (F) of the fluorides, such as fluorite, $CaF_2$. As fluorite shows, more than one atom of an element may be needed to strike the proper electrical balance with another element.

Further common groups are the carbonates composed of a positive group or metal with the $CO_3$ group, such as calcite, which is $CaCO_3$, and malachite, which is $CuCO_3.Cu(OH)_2$. Malachite is more complex than calcite; it includes a second group of copper and an OH group (hydroxyl) to indicate it contains water. Sulphates are compounds of the positive element with $SO_4$, the sulphate group, such as gypsum, $CaSO_4.2H_2O$, which is a hydrous sulphate. Cerussite, $PbSO_4$, lead sulphate, is a less complex one. The phosphates are much like the sulphates, and are written $PO_4$, such as fluor-apatite, $(CaF)Ca_4(PO_4)_3$, a calcium phosphate containing fluorine.

The largest single class, and the most complex, is that of the silicates, which include many of the gem minerals and other hard species, as well as fibrous and sheety ones, such as mica. The silicate molecule is written $SiO_4$. Quartz is silicon dioxide (di- for two), so that it is an oxide but is usually classified as a silicate.

A simple silicate is orthoclase, a feldspar, which is written $KA1Si_3O_8$; the molecules sharing some atoms of oxygen.

The names of minerals give some clues to their chemical makeup. The compounds of two elements often end in -ide, as sodium chloride, salt. Minerals with names ending in -ate are presumably compounds of metals with an acid ending in -ic, such as sulphuric acid, i.e., sulphates, like barite, which is barium sulphate.

# Simple Chemical Tests for Minerals

Many of these tests involve heating the specimen in the flame of a candle, bunsen burner or alcohol lamp and blowing the flame onto the specimen by a blowpipe. Such a flame is made up of an inner blue cone of unburned fuel and air, and around it an area where carbon monoxide and hydrogen are burned with the air to make heat and light. Outside both cones lies an almost invisible zone of burned gases.

The area surrounding the blue inner cone is rich in unoxidized gases, so that it takes oxygen from the specimen. For this reason it is known as the *reducing* flame. In the outer area of burned gases, a specimen may take on oxygen (be oxidized), and this is known as the *oxidizing* flame. The propane hand torch used for silver soldering is an excellent source of the flame if the tip is adjusted to give a normal flame. This would take the place of both the bunsen burner and the blowpipe.

The fusibility of a mineral can be measured by holding a splinter of the mineral in tweezers or forceps in the flame or by directing the flame onto the splinter with a blowpipe (Fig. A). It may fuse easily in the outer, cooler part of the flame, or with difficulty in the hot, inner blue cone. Minerals difficult to fuse may only round on the edges. The following scale is a guide to determining mineral fusibility:

1. Stibnite fuses easily in outer flame.
2. Chalcopyrite fuses in outer flame.
3. Almandine garnet fuses readily under blowpipe.
4. Actinolite's edges round readily under blowpipe.
5. Orthoclase feldspar's edges round with difficulty.
6. Quartz, infusible.

Other blowpipe tests are made by placing a fragment or powder from the mineral in a small

Fig. A. Blowpipe being used to direct candle flame onto mineral fragment held in forceps to test fusibility of mineral. Flame cones are the blue (inner) flame (A), the pale violet, almost invisible, reducing flame (B), and the yellow (outer) or oxidizing flame (C). When flame is blown nearly level with the tip of the blowpipe, the mineral sample is held in forceps outside the tip of the B flame to oxidize it, and just inside the B flame to reduce it. Choose a sharp, pointed sample and take a deep breath for blowing because a constant even flame must be maintained.

Fig. B. Blowpipe being used to direct candle flame onto mineral fragment on charcoal block. Metallic minerals are reduced to metal, and sublimate color is clue to nature of mineral.

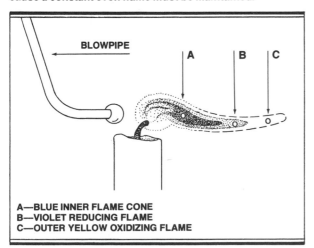

BLOWPIPE

A | B | C

A—BLUE INNER FLAME CONE
B—VIOLET REDUCING FLAME
C—OUTER YELLOW OXIDIZING FLAME

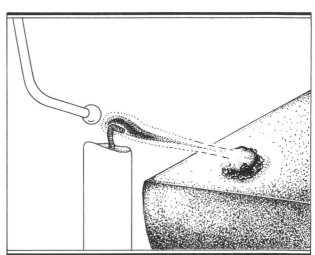

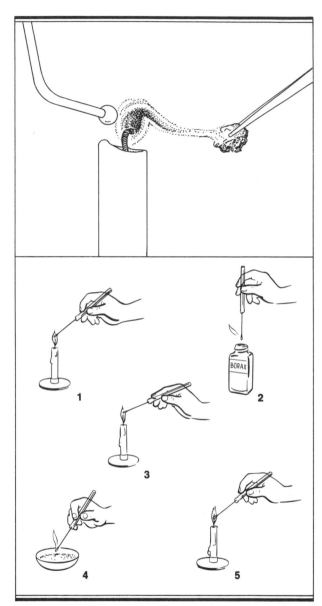

**Fig. C. Blowpipe being used to direct candle flame onto bed of melted borax and powdered mineral for color test of nature of mineral.**

are made with a loop of platinum wire. It should be cleaned after use. Here are tests for elements found in many minerals that can be helpful in their identification:

Aluminum: Infusible aluminum minerals, powdered and heated in the oxidizing flame, become blue when moistened with cobalt nitrate ($Co_2NO_3$).

Antimony: Most antimony compounds yield a white sublimate on the charcoal block under the oxidizing flame.

Arsenic: When heated in the reducing flame, most arsenic compounds give off a garlic-like odor and form a white coating on the charcoal block.

Barium: Barium minerals color the burner flame yellowish green. For the test, the mineral is powdered, moistened with hydrochloric acid ($HCl$) and held in the flame on a platinum wire loop.

Bismuth: Bismuth minerals yield brittle beads of the metal if mixed with three times as much sodium carbonate ($Na_2CO_3$) and heated in the reducing flame. An orange sublimate also forms.

Boron: Boron minerals impart a bright green color to the flame. Moisten specimen with dilute sulphuric acid ($H_2SO_4$) before testing it.

Calcium: Many calcium minerals, powdered and moistened with HCl, color the flame yellowish red.

Carbonates: Carbonate minerals effervesce in a dilute acid, some freely and some with difficulty. Dolomite must be powdered or placed in warm acid to react.

Chromium: Chromium responds to a bead test. A bead of borax is formed in a loop of platinum wire and is just touched to a powdered chromium mineral. When reheated in the oxidizing flame the bead will turn yellow, and then turn green in the reducing flame.

Cobalt: A similar test with a cobalt mineral will color the borax bead a deep blue.

Copper: A copper mineral dissolved in nitric acid ($HNO_3$) in a test tube forms a green solution that turns deep blue when ammonia ($NH_4OH$) is added.

depression dug into the surface of a charcoal block. While the block is held near the flame, the blowpipe directs flame onto the specimen as in Figure B.

The reducing flame will convert powdered ore of gold, silver, tin, lead or copper, mixed with three times as much powdered borax, to a small button of the metal itself. Other minerals form a coating or sublimate on the charcoal block, or color the flame. Colors imparted to a bead of borax in the flame are clues in another detective method open to the amateur (Fig. C). Bead tests

Lead: A lead mineral dissolved in $HNO_3$ in a test tube throws down a white precipitate when HCl is added.

Iron: A ferric iron mineral boiled in $HNO_3$ in a test tube forms a red brown precipitate when $NH_4OH$ is added. Iron minerals also become magnetic after being roasted in the reducing flame.

Lithium: Lithium's presence in a mineral is indicated by the brilliant crimson color of the flame in which a fragment is held.

Manganese: A manganese mineral, powdered and fused in a bead of $Na_2CO_3$ in an oxidizing flame, colors the cool bead a bluish green. It will color a borax bead violet red but the color disappears in a reducing flame.

Magnesium: Heat in flame, moisten with cobalt nitrate solution, and heat again. Some compounds turn pink.

Mercury: A mercury mineral heated with $Na_2CO_3$ in a closed tube which is a glass tube bent at a 45-degree angle 2 inches from one end closed by fusing the tubing, deposits gray globules of mercury on the cool upper walls of the tube.

Molybdenum: Molybdenite (MoS) heated on charcoal in the oxidizing flame forms a sublimate that is pale yellow while hot, white when cold, and blue in the reducing flame.

Nickel: The presence of nickel in a mineral is disclosed by dissolving it in $HNO_3$, neutralizing the solution with $NH_4OH$ and adding a few drops of dimethylglyoxime, forming a scarlet precipitate.

Phosphate: A phosphate mineral dissolved in cold $HNO_3$ and added to a cold solution of ammonium molybdate forms a yellow precipitate.

Potassium: The powdered mineral mixed with an equal part of powdered gypsum ($CaSO_4 2H_2O$) and heated on a platinum wire in the flame turns it a pale violet. The color is more easily detected by looking at the flame through a blue glass to filter out the yellowish flame color of sodium.

Selenium: Selenium minerals give off a horse-radish odor in the flame and color it an intense blue.

Silver: A silver mineral dissolved in $HNO_3$ throws down a white precipitate when HCl is added. The precipitate will turn purple in strong sunlight.

Sodium: Sodium minerals color the flame intense yellow.

Strontium: A strontium mineral powdered and moistened with HCl turns the flame crimson, much like lithium.

Sulphates: These minerals, dissolved in dilute HCl, form a dense white precipitate when barium chloride is added.

Sulphides: These minerals give off the pungent odor of sulphur dioxide when heated in the flame.

Tin: A fragment of tin mineral, placed in warm dilute HCl with a granule of zinc metal, develops a shiny coating of metallic tin.

Titanium: A titanium mineral fused with five times as much $Na_2CO_3$ on charcoal, and the fused material dissolved in sulphuric acid ($H_2SO_4$), heated until clear, allowed to cool and diluted with distilled water, will turn the solution yellow to amber when hydrogen peroxide is added.

Tungsten: A tungsten mineral powdered and fused with $Na_2CO_3$, and the fusion powdered, boiled in water in a test tube and filtered, gives a white precipitate when HCl is added. The precipitate turns yellow when the solution is boiled.

Uranium: A borax bead touched to a powdered uranium mineral and fused will fluoresce green under ultraviolet light.

Vanadium: When fused with borax vanadium minerals form a yellow bead that turns yellowish-green, then loses color as it cools.

Water: Water in a hydrous mineral is detected by heating small fragments of the mineral in the bend of a closed tube until very hot. Water will collect on the cool upper walls. Gypsum can be distinguished from anhydrite, which contains no water, by this test.

Zinc: Zinc silicates moistened with cobalt nitrate solution and heated in the oxidizing flame turn blue; other zinc minerals turn green.

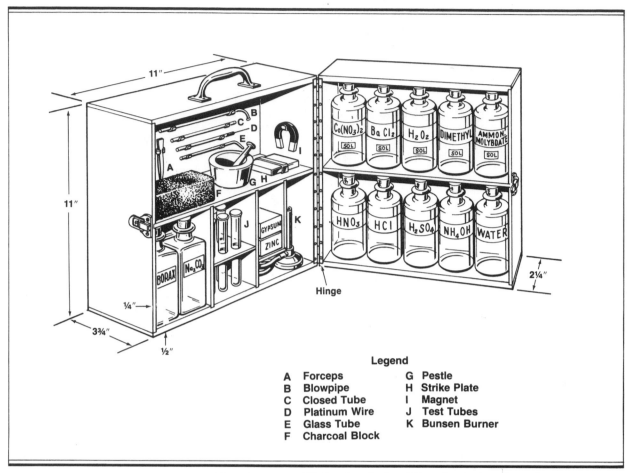

**Legend**

A Forceps      G Pestle
B Blowpipe      H Strike Plate
C Closed Tube      I Magnet
D Platinum Wire      J Test Tubes
E Glass Tube      K Bunsen Burner
F Charcoal Block

**Fig. D.** A double case hinged on one side makes a good kit for chemical and blowpipe test equipment.

An ideal kit for chemical and blowpipe determinations is shown in Figure D. It is essentially a double case hinged on the side so that it will swing open and stand upright. Each side of the case has ½ inch tops and bottoms to which ¼ inch plywood sides and back are nailed. But one side has an interior depth of 2¼ inches and the other of 3¾ inches. Each side is divided midway horizontally by a ½ inch shelf, and the deeper side is also divided into compartments. The sides are held together with a latch and have a handle on top for carrying.

In the shallower side are 4-ounce, glass-stoppered bottles for nitric, hydrochloric and sulphuric acids, ammonia and distilled water, and for solutions of cobalt nitrate, barium chloride, hydrogen peroxide, dimethylglyoxime and ammonium molybdate.

In the deeper side are bottles for borax and sodium carbonate, small boxes for gypsum and zinc metal, a bunsen burner, six test tubes 4 inches tall in a removable rack, a charcoal block,

mortar and pestle, streak plate, small horseshoe magnet, a 6-inch glass tube and a 6-inch closed glass tube, steel forceps or tweezers, a 2-inch piece of platinum wire fused into a glass tube handle, a blowpipe, and a set of hardness testers or a small box containing crystals of quartz, topaz and corundum for testing hardness.

The box should be enameled or finished with chemical-resistant paint inside. Outside it may be stained and varnished. The shelves are proportioned so that the acid and other reagent bottles fit closely, but care should be used that strong acids are not spilled.

The dilutions of the liquid reagents you will need are:

Barium chloride, 12 grams of $BaCl_2 2H_2O$ in 100 cc. of distilled water.

Cobalt Nitrate, saturated solution.

Dimethylglyoxime, dissolve one gram in 100 cc. of 95 per cent ethyl alcohol.

Hydrochloric acid, dilute, 35 cc. of concentrated HCl to 100 cc. water.

Hydrogen peroxide, the commercial 3 per cent solution.

Nitric acid, 35 cc of concentrated $HNO_3$ to 100 cc. of water. Ammonia, dilute, 10 cc. of the concentrated $NH_4OH$ in 20 cc. of water.

Ammonium molybdate, dissolve 15 grams of $(NH_4)_2MoO_4$ in 300 cc. of water and pour into 100 cc. of $HNO_3$ (sp.g.1.2).

Sulphuric acid, dilute, pour 20 cc. of concentrated $H_2SO_4$ slowly and with constant stirring into 80 cc. of water. (NOTE: *Never add water to any acid,* as this causes great heat and may cause the solution to boil and spray skin and clothing. REMEMBER AAA: Always Add Acid to the water.)

# Key to Invertebrate Fossils

*Fossil types*

A. With radial symmetry
   1. Tapering and cylindrical
      a. Longitudinal partitions and cone shaped      Coral
      b. Shell with transverse partitions, tapering    Cephalopod
      c. Shell lacking internal partitions
         1) Large with external ribs, Cretaceous    Rudistid
         2) Small, open both ends    Scaphopod
   2. Disk or flattened dome
      a. Star pattern on top    Echinoid
      b. Dome shaped with flat base, surface covered with pores, small    Bryozoa
      c. Disk shaped, less than ½ inch in diameter    Foraminifera
      d. Disk with longitudinal partitions    Coral
   3. Segments or plates
      a. Circular segments forming tapered cylinder    Cephalopod
      b. Circular segments, small, hole in center    Crinoid stem
      c. Bud shaped, 13 wedge-shaped plates    Blastoid
      d. Cup shaped, many curved plates, branching arms    Crinoid head

# I Radial Symmetry

## A. TAPERING, CYLINDRICAL CONE-SHAPED FOSSILS

**1. Cone-shaped with longitudinal partitions or septa**
CORAL

**2. Fossils with septa or sutures; tapering at one end**
CEPHALOPOD

**3. Shell without internal partitions or sutures**

**a. Shell large heavy, external longitudinal ribs. Cretaceous only**
RUDISTID

**b. Shell small, tusk-shaped open at both ends. Rare in Paleozoic and Mesozoic**
SCAPHOPOD

## B. DISC OR DOME-SHAPED FOSSILS

**1. Star pattern on top**
ECHINOID

**2. Subconical small pits or pores on top**
BRYOZOAN

**3. Small disc-shaped (less than ½ inch)**
ORBITOID FORAMINIFERA

**4. Disc-shaped or button-like, with longitudinal partitions or septa**
CORAL

## C. FOSSILS COMPOSED OF SEGMENTS OR PLATES

**1. Circular discs or chambers; when united form cylinder**

**a. Tapered shell**
CEPHALOPOD

**b. Not tapered, segments small of uniform thickness, hole in center**
CRINOID STEM

**2. Fossil composed of many-sided plates**

**a. Bud-shaped, 13 wedge-shaped plates**
BLASTOID

**b. Cup-shaped, many curved plates branching arms**
CRINOID

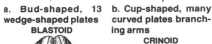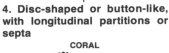

*Fossil types*

B. With bilateral symmetry
    1. Coiled in single plane
        a. Shell divided by transverse internal partitions        Cephalopod
        b. Shell lacking internal partitions        Gastropod
        c. Shell small, like wheat grain        Foraminifera
    2. Not coiled
        a. Shells like clams
            1) Symmetry line along hinge        Pelecypod
            2) Symmetry line at right angles to hinge line, ribbed like scallop        Pelecypod
            3) Symmetry line at right angles to hinge line, unlike scallops        Brachiopod
        b. Cylindrical, cone shaped
            1) Cone shaped, longitudinal partitions        Coral
            2) Shell with internal transverse partitions, tapering        Cephalopod
            3) Shell lacking internal partitions, large, ribbed        Rudistid
            4) Shell lacking partitions, small, open on both ends        Scaphopod
        c. Heart shaped, domed, star pattern on top        Echinoid
        d. Segmented, 3 lobes, often curled        Trilobite
        e. Segmented, flattened, like shrimp        Crustacean

# II  Bilateral Symmetry

## A.  FOSSIL COILED IN A SINGLE PLANE

**1.** Shell divided by internal transverse partitions or sutures
**CEPHALOPOD**

**2.** Shell without internal partitions or sutures
**GASTROPOD**

**3.** Shell small, spindle-shaped; resembles wheat grain. Pennsylvanian and Permian
**FORAMINIFERA**
**FUSULINID**

## B.  FOSSIL NOT COILED

**1.** Shells or valves similar to clams

**a.** Plane of symmetry parallel to hinge; equivalved
**PELECYPOD**

**b.** Plane of symmetry almost at right angles to hinge; strongly ribbed; "Scalloplike" with "ears", inequivalved
**PELECYPOD**

**c.** Plane of symmetry at right angles to hinge-line; without "ears", not "Scallop-like"; commonly with opening in beak, inequivalved
**BRACHIOPOD**

**3.** Fossil heart-shaped domed or flattened; star pattern on top
**ECHINOID**

**4.** Fossil segmented

**a.** Divided into 3 lobes, may be curled up, Paleozoic only
**TRILOBITE**

**b.** Flattened or elongate, resembles shrimp
**CRUSTACEAN**

**2.** Fossil tapering, cylindrical or cone-shaped

**a.** Cone-shaped, internal longitudinal partitions or septa
**CORAL**

**b.** Tapered, internal transverse partitions
**CEPHALOPOD**

**c.** Shell without internal septa or partitions

**(1.)** Shell large heavy, longitudinal ribs Cretaceous only
**RUDISTID**

**(2.)** Shell small, tusk-shaped, open at both ends, rare in Paleozoic and Mesozoic rocks
**SCAPHOPOD**

*Fossil types*

C. Lacking symmetry
    1. Shell without transverse internal partitions
        a. Coiled like horn, concentric ridges on two valves      Pelecypod
        b. Tightly coiled, single valve smoother      Gastropod
    2. Coiled but not in single plane
        a. Shell with transverse partitions
            1) Partitions smooth, loosely coiled, in masses      Caprinid
            2) Partitions wrinkled, tightly coiled      Cephalopod
        b. Shell without transverse internal partitions      Gastropod
        c. Spiral ridge like corkscrew      Bryozoa
    3. Uncoiled
        a. Black narrow blade      Graptolite
        b. Cone shaped, radial partitions      Coral
        c. Shell like oyster      Pelecypod
        d. Branching or twiglike
            1) Surface covered with pores      Bryozoa
            2) Pattern of large openings, with radial partitions      Colonial Coral
        e. Lacy and filmlike      Bryozoa
        f. Masses of five-sided or round tubes with radial partitions      Colonial Coral
        g. Roughly cylindrical, irregular surface, thick-walled, ribbed      Rudistid
        h. Solid with pitted surface      Sponge

NOTE: Rudistid and caprinid are found only in Cretaceous rocks. Scaphopod usually found in Cenozoic rocks. Foraminifera usually found in late Paleozoic rocks. Brachiopods are common in Paleozoic rocks, and trilobites are limited to that era, along with graptolites.
(Adapted from outline published by Bureau of Economic Geology, The University of Texas, and used by permission.)

# III No Apparent Symmetry

## A. SHELL WITHOUT TRANSVERSE PARTITIONS OR SUTURES

**1.** Shell coiled like ram's horn, low spired; shell has two valves, smaller flattened valve often missing. In Texas exclusively Cretaceous
**PELECYPOD**

**2.** Shell tightly coiled, most have higher spire than 1, shell smaller and not as rough as 1, has only one valve
**GASTROPOD**

## B. COILED FOSSILS, COILING NOT IN ONE PLANE

**1.** Shell with transverse internal partitions or sutures

**2.** Shell without transverse internal partitions or sutures
**GASTROPOD**

**3.** Solid spiral ridge around central axis, resembles corkscrew
**BRYOZOAN**

**a.** Partitions always smooth, thick shelled, loosely and irregularly coiled, in Texas exclusively Cretaceous
**CAPRINID**

**b.** Partitions (sutures) generally wrinkled, regularly and tightly coiled
**CEPHALOPOD**

## C. UNCOILED FOSSILS

**1.** Fossil resembles narrow saw blade, Paleozoic only
**GRAPTOLITE**

**3.** Shell resembles clam or oyster, nonsymmetrical
**PELECYPOD (MOSTLY OYSTERS)**

**5.** Lace-like fossils, occur as thin sheets or films
**BRYOZOA**

**7.** Irregular fossils, cylindrical with rough surface

**a.** Large axial opening with thick wall, external longitudinal ribs, Cretaceous only
**RUDISTID**

**b.** Solid, no opening, small pits or pores Pennsylvanian or Permian
**SPONGE**

**2.** Fossil irregularly cone-shaped, longitudinal partitions or septa
**CORAL**

**4.** Branching twig-like fossils

**6.** Masses of circular or polygonal tubes with septa
**COLONIAL CORAL**

**a.** Covered with minute pores or openings
**BRYOZOA**

**b.** With evenly distributed larger openings with septa
**COLONIAL CORAL**

# Sources of Information

## Books on Geology

*Down to Earth, an Introduction to Geology,* Carey Croneis and William C. Krumbein. University of Chicago Press, 1936. 499 pp. Also in paperback. Old but comprehensive and rewardingly readable.

*Causes of Catastrophe,* Don Leet. New York, McGraw Hill Book Co., 1938, 232 pp.
Still useful account of hurricanes, volcanoes and earthquakes.

*Geology* (2d ed.) William C. Putnam. Oxford University Press, 1971, 585 pp.
Exceptionally well written and well organized textbook.

*Geology of Michigan,* John A. Dorr Jr. and Donald F. Eschmann. Ann Arbor, University of Michigan Press, 1970, 476 pp.
General treatment of geology with specialized application; admirably illustrated.

*The Earth Beneath Us,* Kirtley F. Mather. New York: Random House, 1964, 320 pp.
Magnificent illustrations augment the eloquent prose of a noted teacher.

*Geology of the Great Lakes,* J. L. Hough. Urbana: University of Illinois Press, 1958, 313 pp.
Well written and authoritative account of one of the nation's major geological treasures.

*Principles of Geology, (4th ed.),* J. Gilluly, A. C. Waters and A. O. Woodford. San Francisco: W. H. Freeman & Co., 1975, 527 pp.
A standard and highly regarded textbook.

*The Restless Earth,* Nigel Calder. New York: Viking Press, 1972, 152 pp.
Popular account of the new geology.

*Rock, Time and Landforms,* Jerome Wykoff. New York: Harper & Row, 1966, 372 pp.
The story of the geological forces that shape the landscape, well told.

*Dictionary of Geological Terms,* Garden City: Doubleday & Co., 1962, 545 pp. Dolphin paperback.
Useful reference book prepared by the American Geological Institute.

## Books on Rocks, Minerals and Gems

*Encyclopedia of Minerals,* Willard L. Roberts, George R. Rapp Jr. and Julius Weber. New York: Van Nostrand-Reinhold Co., 1974, 693 pp.
Expensive but one of the most comprehensive treatments with many color illustrations of reference value.

*A Field Guide to Rocks and Minerals* (4th ed.) Frederick H. Pough. Boston: Houghton Mifflin Co., 1976, 336 pp.
Useful member of a noted series of guidebooks by an authority.

*Getting Acquainted With Minerals,* George L. English and David E. Jensen. New York: McGraw Hill Co., 1959, 362 pp.
A classic brought up to date.

*A Guide to Minerals, Rocks and Fossils,* W. R. Hamilton, A. R. Wolley and A. C. Bishop. New York: Crescent Books, 1974, 319 pp.
British publication with exceptionally useful color illustrations and short descriptions of species.

*Mineralogy of Arizona,* John W. Anthony, Sidney A. Williams and Richard A. Bideaux. Tucson, University of Arizona Press, 241 pp., 1977. Also paperback.
New and authoritative guide whose usefulness extends beyond its state borders. Excellent bibliography.

*Mineralogy for Amateurs,* John Sinkankas. New York: Van Nostrand Reinhold Co., 1964, 585 pp. Also in paperback.
Detailed and clearly written introduction to a difficult subject.

*The Rockhound's Manual,* Gordon S. Fay. New York: Barnes & Noble, 1972, 290 pp. Paperback.
General treatment of collecting, especially rich in sources of information.

*The Rock Book,* Carroll Lane and Mildred Adams Fenton. Garden City: Doubleday & Co., 1940, 257 pp.
Old but still a recommended popular book, well illustrated.

*Rocks and Minerals,* Joel Arem. New York, Ridge Press, 1973, 145 pp. Paperback.
Brief but surprisingly adequate treatment with much color.

*Dana's Manual on Mineralogy* (18th ed.) by Edward Salisbury Dana, revised by Cornelius S. Hurlbut, Jr.: John Wiley & Sons, Inc., 579 pp.
Best single volume reference book, newly revised.

*Ultraviolet Guide to Minerals,* Sterling Gleason. New York: Van Nostrand Reinhold Co., 1960, 244 pp.
Somewhat dated but still a useful guide in its specialized field.

*The Curious Lore of Precious Stones,* George F. Kunz. Philadelphia, J. B. Lippincott Co., 1913, 406 pp.
Classic account of the folklore of gems and stones, by a celebrated collector.

*Gem Hunter's Guide* (5th ed.), Russell P. MacFall. New York: Thomas Y. Crowell Co., 1976, 323 pp.
What the collector wants to know about field trips, with the most complete listings of locations.

*Gems and Jewelry,* Joel Arem. New York: Ridge Press, 1975, 159 pp. Bantam Books paperback.
Brief but readable introduction to the subject, with good color.

*Prospecting for Gemstones and Minerals,* John Sinkankas. New York: Van Nostrand Reinhold Co., 1970, 397 pp. Also paperback.
Methods of prospecting and collecting, recognition of rocks and mineral deposits, preparation of specimens.

*Cleaning and Preserving Minerals* (4th ed.), Richard M. Pearl. Earth Science Publishing Co., Colorado Springs: 1976, 86 pp.
Only specialized publication of its kind, kept up to date by frequent revision.

*Crystals and Crystal Growing,* Alan Holden and Phyllis Singer. Garden City: Doubleday & Co., 1960, 320 pp. Paperback.
Learning about the ways of crystals by growing them, highly recommended.

## Books on Fossils

*Fossils for Amateurs,* Russel P. Mac Fall and Jay C. Wollin. New York: Van Nostrand Reinhold Co., 1971, 341 pp.
Comprehensive treatment of collecting, preparing and identifying invertebrate fossils.

*Invertebrate Fossils,* R. C. Moore, C. G. Lalicker and A. G. Fischer. New York, McGraw Hill Co., 1952.
Recommended general introductory text.

*Life of the Past,* George Gaylord Simpson. New Haven: Yale University Press, 1953, 198 pp. Paperback.
A delightful introduction to paleontology by a scholar who can write.

*Fossils,* William H. Matthews III. New York: Barnes & Noble, 1962, 336 pp. paperback.
Comprehensive view of both invertebrate and vertebrate fossil life.

*The Fossil Book,* Carroll Lane and Mildred Adams Fenton. Garden City: Doubleday & Co., 1958. 482 pp.
Generously illustrated, well written, a basic book for the amateur.

*Search for the Past,* James R. Beerbower. Englewood Cliffs, N.J.: Prentice Hall Co., 1960, 562 pp.
Good reading and authoritative information.

*The Bone Hunters,* by Url Lanham. New York: Columbia University Press, 1973, 285 pp.
Just what you would want to know about the great vertebrate fossil collectors.

*Before the Deluge,* Herbert Wendt. Garden City, N.Y.: Doubleday & Co., 1968, 419 pp.
Highly recommended popular discussion of the history of fossil legend and science.

## Books on Lapidary Techniques

*The Art of the Lapidary,* Francis J. Sperisen. Milwaukee: Bruce Publishing Co., 1950, 382 pp.
Comprehensive and sound technical information.

*Gem Cutting, A Lapidaries Manual,* John Sinkankas, Van Nostrand Reinhold Co., 1962, 297 pp. Paperback.
An authoritative guide to various lapidary techniques.

## Magazine

The Lapidary Journal
P.O. Box 80937
San Diego, Calif. 92138

# Sources of Lapidary Equipment and Supplies

Allcraft Tool and Supply Co. Inc.
215 Park Avenue, Hicksville, New York 11801

Covington Engineering Corp.
P.O. Box 35
Redlands, Calif. 92373

Beacon Engineering Co.,
Rothsay
Minnesota

Copace Corp.
2249 Charing Cross Road
Baldwin, N.Y. 11510

Crystalite Corporation
P.O. Box 9400
13449 Beach Avenue
Marina Del Ray, Calif. 90291

Gem and Mineral Display Co.
P.O. Box 22145
Phoenix, Ariz. 85028

Geode Industries
106-108 W. Main, Highway 34
New London, Iowa 52645

Keene Engineering Co. (prospecting equipment)
11483 Vanowen Street
North Hollywood, Calif. 91605

Raytech Industries, Inc.
(lapidary and ultraviolet products)
P.O. Box 84
Stafford Springs, Ct. 06076

Shop-Vac Corporation
2323 Reach Road
Williamsport, Pa. 17701

Star Diamond Industries
1421 West 240th Street
Harbor City, Calif. 90710

Ward's Natural Science Establishment
P.O. Box 1712
Rochester 3, New York

# Glossary

| | |
|---|---|
| Adamantine | having a brilliant luster, like that of a diamond. |
| Aluminum or bronze rods or pencils | tools for marking minerals to be cut. |
| Angstrom unit | unit for measuring wavelengths of light used in detecting fluorescence and phosphorescence in minerals. |
| Asteriated | reflecting light in star ray pattern, characteristic of some forms of sapphire, ruby, quartz, spinel, garnet, chrysoberyl, and mica. |
| Balas ruby | term formerly used for forms of spinel, rubellite and other stones that resembled rubies. |
| Bead test | Identifying nature of mineral by color it gives when fused in a bead of borax held in a flame. |
| Bezel | top part of gemstone mounting that surrounds or holds the stone. |
| Black light | common name for light from filtered ultraviolet ray lamp used to determine fluorescence or phosphorescence. |
| Black sand | dark magnetic sand, associated with gold flakes, that can be separated from the non-magnetic gold with a magnet. |
| Blowpipe | metal tube that tapers to small curved end, used in making tests to determine identity of mineral. |
| Brazilian topaz | yellowish citrine quartz resembling topaz. |
| Brilliant cut | familiar round cut gemstone with 58 polished flat faces or facets. |
| Cabochon | usually round or oval-shaped gem with domed top, flat bottom and no facets. |
| Chatoyancy | ability of a mineral to reflect silky sheen of light from the fibers inside it, as in tigerseye, satin spar and catseye. |
| Chrysanthemum or flower rock | crystals embedded in rock to form a flower-like pattern. |
| Cleavage | planes along which a mineral will naturally separate when split; not all minerals have natural cleavage. |
| "Color" | prospector's term for small flakes of gold. |

| | |
|---|---|
| Conchoidal | curved concave shape like the inside of a seashell that occurs when minerals like quartz, opal and glass are chipped or fractured. |
| Contact goniometer | shop protractor with pivoting head for measuring the interfacial angles of mineral crystals. |
| Crown | upper portion of a faceted gemstone, extending from widest part (girdle) to flat table on top. |
| Crystal | mineral with organized internal structure usually expressed by external plane surfaces or faces that meet at characteristic angles. |
| Crystallography | the study of crystals. |
| Culet | the bottom point of a faceted gemstone. |
| Desert varnish | mahogany colored coating on surface of exposed rocks, caused by weathering. |
| Diamond blade | saw blade with diamond fragments embedded in its edge, for cutting minerals. |
| Dop or dopstick | wood or metal rod to which gemstone is mounted for shaping and polishing. |
| Dopping | fixing gemstone to dop to hold it while shaping and polishing. |
| Dopping stove | unit for heating stone and wax at same time before mounting on dopstick. |
| Double refraction | ability of some minerals such as transparent calcite to divide one ray of light into two rays so that double image is seen through it. |
| Dredging | using machinery that works like vacuum cleaner to suck materials from bottom of streams and run it through sluice that separates out heavy metals like gold. |
| Dry placer | dirt or gravelly area such as old stream bed worked for gold without water. |
| Earthy | earth-like surface appearance of some minerals. |
| Facet | flat plane cut on surface of gem at a specific angle to help it bounce or refract light back through top or crown of stone. |
| Faceting machine | machine for cutting facets in gemstones. |
| Fibrous or splintery | appearance of fractured or broken surface characteristic of some minerals or rocks. |
| Findings | small metal jewelry parts used by lapidaries for mounting gemstones. |
| Fish eye | stone faceted badly so light leaks out of pavilion and you can see through stone. |
| Flat | thin slice sawed from a thicker chunk of mineral or rock. |
| Float | separate chunk or mass of ore found near surface. |
| Flour gold | tiny flecks or flakes of gold, frequently found with black sand. |

| | |
|---|---|
| Fluorescence | glowing color reaction of a mineral while it is exposed to invisible ultraviolet rays. |
| Fool's gold | any of various forms of pyrite that are frequently mistaken for real gold. |
| Fossil | evidence of once-living organism preserved in rocks and minerals. |
| Fracture | chipped or broken surface of a rock or mineral. |
| Gemstone | any stone used for lapidary work. |
| Girdle | widest part of a cut gem separating the top (crown) from the base (pavilion). |
| Glassy | surface luster of some minerals, such as opal and quartz. |
| Gold pan | shallow pan used by prospectors to separate gold from associated dirt and gravel. |
| Greasy | surface luster of some minerals, such as serpentine. |
| Hackly | jagged surface of minerals, such as copper, when broken. |
| Hardness | resistance to surface scratching of a mineral. |
| Herkimer "diamonds" | clear quartz crystals found in or near Herkimer County, New York. |
| Igneous | rock formed when molten material solidifies. |
| Interfacial angle | angle formed where two faces of a crystal meet, as the 60-degree angles of hexagonal corundum. |
| Iridescent | showing rainbow play of colors as mineral is turned. |
| Lap or lap wheel | circular wheel for smoothing and polishing flat gem materials. |
| Lapidary | one who fashions or works with gem minerals. |
| Lapping | smoothing and polishing flat surface of mineral or gem on a lap wheel. |
| Lode | mineral vein or mass of ore embedded in rock. |
| Long wave | ultraviolet light of about 3660 angstrom unit wavelength. |
| Luster | surface appearance of an unbroken mineral. |
| Matrix | rock to which a mineral specimen is attached or in which it is embedded. |
| Matura "diamonds" | small, colorless zircon crystals found near Matura in Ceylon. |
| Metallic | surface luster of some minerals, notably the metals and sulphides. |
| Metamorphic | name for rock that has been changed from its original state by pressure, heat, gases or chemicals. |
| Meteoritics | the study of things from the sky. |

| | |
|---|---|
| Mineral | inorganic substance with a definite chemical composition and an orderly internal atomic structure. |
| Mohs scale | scale from 1 to 10 for determining relative surface hardness or resistance to scratching of various minerals. |
| Mounting | material in which gemstone is held. |
| Nodule | small rounded lump in a cavity in rock. |
| Nugget | small lump of precious metal in its natural state. |
| Paleontology | the study of fossils. |
| Panning | using a gold pan to separate gold particles from associated dirt and gravel. |
| Pavilion | lower part of a cut gem, extending from the girdle to the culet. |
| Pearly | having a pearl-like surface luster, like the cleavage of feldspar. |
| Petrology | the study of rocks. |
| Phosphorescence | continued glowing reaction of a mineral after it has been exposed to ultraviolet rays and the source of the rays has been removed. |
| Placer gold | loose gold deposits found in dirt and gravel at bottom of riverbeds and streams. |
| Porphyry | crystals of minerals showing against background of fine-grained rock; see chrysanthemum or flower rock. |
| Precious stones | gems generally having the greatest value, as diamond, ruby, sapphire, emerald, opal. |
| Preform | gem cut to general outlines of final shape but not yet completed. |
| Prospector's pick | hammer-like tool with one blunt end and one sharp pointed end. |
| Pudding stone | pebbles and sand cemented together in a hard rock. |
| Resinous | having a surface luster like that of resin. |
| Riffle box | prospector's metal chute lined with removable slats or riffles that catch heavy metal particles and let them fall through mesh to mat underneath. |
| Rock | natural inorganic solid made up primarily of a mixture of minerals. |
| Rough | gem material that has not been cut. |
| Sedimentary | rock formed from remains of other rocks or organisms, or by precipitation from chemical solutions. |
| Semiprecious stones | stones cut and used as gems but of lesser value than precious stones. |
| Short wave | ultraviolet light of about 2537 angstrom unit wavelength. |

| | |
|---|---|
| Skarn | rock containing such minerals as garnet, epidote, idocrase and diopside, silicates formed by intrusion of hot magma into limestone. |
| Silky | surface luster of some minerals, such as asbestos and satin spar. |
| Slab | flat slice of mineral. |
| Slicks | wind-polished pieces such as jade found on the surface. |
| Sloughing off | spilling water and light debris over edge of gold pan to separate it from heavier gold. |
| Sniping tool | metal rod with bent ends, one ending in point, the other in shallow spoon; used for digging in crevices and spooning up samples to check for precious metals. |
| Specific gravity | comparison of weight of a mineral with the weight of an equal volume of water. |
| Spectrographic analysis | identifying mineral by determining the wavelengths in the color absorption spectra of its components. |
| Speleology | the study of caves. |
| Splintery | appearance of broken or fractured surfaces of some minerals like jade. |
| Streak | powdery mark left by mineral when scratched across unglazed tile or frosted glass; color of mark helps identify mineral. |
| Swiss lapis | chalcedony dyed to resemble lapis lazuli. |
| Table | flat surface on top of a faceted gem. |
| Thunder eggs | rounded nodules or geodes of agate or opal formed in gas pockets of decomposed lava in parts of Washington, Oregon, Idaho and Montana. |
| Tumbling | rotating or vibrating gemstones in a small barrel with abrasives and water to smooth and polish them. |
| Venus hairs or arrows of love | hairlike needles of rutile embedded in quartz. |
| Vitreous | having a glassy surface luster. |
| Vug | small cavity in a lode or in a rock. |
| Winnowing | separating gold from associated debris by tossing material sieved into blanket so that breeze carries off light debris. |
| X-ray diffraction | using X-rays to visually plot the internal atomic structure of a mineral. |

# Easy Rock and Mineral Pronouncing Vocabulary

| | | | |
|---|---|---|---|
| Abrasive | uh-BRAY-sive | Chalcanthite | kal-KAN-thite |
| Actinolite | ak-TIN-oh-lite | Chalcedony | kal-SED-uh-nee |
| Adamantine | ad-uh-MAN-teen | Chalcocite | KAL-ko-site |
| Agate | AG-it | Chalcopyrite | kal-ku-PIE-rite |
| Alabaster | al-uh-BASS-turr | Chalcotrichite | kal-KOTT-rick-ite |
| Albite | AL-bite | Chiastolite | ky-AS-toe-lite |
| Alexandrite | al-egg-ZAN-drite | Chyrsoberyl | KRISS-uh-beh-rill |
| Almandite | AL-man-dite | Chrysocolla | KRISS-uh-COLL-ah |
| Aluminum | al-LEW-min-um | Chrysoprase | KRISS-o-priase |
| Amber | AM-burr | Chrysotile | KRISS-o-till |
| Amethyst | Am-uh-thist | Cinnabar | SIN-uh-bahr |
| Analcite | ah-NAL-site | Citrine | SIT-rin |
| Andalusite | an duh-LEW-site | Clarkeite | KLARRK-ite |
| Anglesite | ANG-luh-site | Conchoidal | kong-KOY-duhl |
| Antimony | AN-ti-mony | Conglomerate | kon-GLOMM-urr-it |
| Apatite | AP-uh-tite | Corundum | kuh-RUN-dum |
| Apophyllite | ap-POF-ih-lite | Covellite | ko-VELL-ite |
| Aquamarine | ak-wah-muh-REEN | Cristobalite | kriss-TOE-buh-lite |
| Aragonite | uh-RAG-uh-nite | Crocoite | KROW-koh-ite |
| Argentite | AR-jen-tite | Cuprite | KEW-prite |
| Arsenopyrite | AR-sen-oh-PIE-rite | Cyanite | KY-uh-nite |
| Asbestos | ass-BEST-us | | |
| Augite | AW-jite | Dana | DAY-nuh |
| Aurichalcite | OR-ri-CAL-cite | Datolite | DAT-oh-lite |
| Autunite | AW-tun-ite | Dendrite | DEN-drite |
| Aventurine | ah-VEN-shur-in | Descloizite | day-KLOY-zite |
| Azurite | AZH-uh-rite | Diabase | DI-ah-base |
| | | Dinosaur | DY-nuh-sawr |
| Barite | BEAR-ite | Diorite | DY-or-ite |
| Basalt | buh-SALT | Diopside | dy-OPP-side |
| Bauxite | BAWK-site | Dioptase | die-OPP-tase |
| Benitoite | beh-NEE-toe-ite | Dodecahedral | DOH-deck-uh-hee-druhl |
| Beryl | BEH-rill | Dolomite | DOLL-uh-mite |
| Beryllium | beh-RILL-ee-um | Drusy Quartz | DROO-zi-KWARTZ |
| Biotite | BY-oh-tite | Ductile | DUCK-till |
| Breccia | BRETCH-ee-uh | Dumortorite | du-MORE-ter-ite |
| Brucite | BREW-site | | |
| | | Emerald | EM-urr-uld |
| Cabochon | KAB-oh-shun | Enargite | en-AR-jite |
| Calcite | KAL-site | Epidote | EPP-ih-dote |
| Calcium | KAL-see-um | Erythrite | E-RITH-rite |
| Calomine | KAL-ah-min | | |
| Calcareous | kal-KAY-ree-us | Feldspar | FELD-spahr |
| Carnelian | car-NEEL-yun | Fluorescence | floo-uh-RESS-sence |
| Celestite | SELL-est-ite | Fluorite | FLOO-uh-rite |
| Cerussite | SEE-ruh-site | Fulgerite | FULG-your-rite |
| Cervantite | sur-VAN-tite | Galena | gaa-LEE-na |

| | | | |
|---|---|---|---|
| Gangue | Gang | Pectolite | PECK-toh-lite |
| Garnet | GAHR-net | Pegmatite | PEG-muh-tite |
| Gastrolith | GAS-truh-lite | Peridot | PERR-ih-dot |
| Genthite | GENN-thite | Phosphate | FOSS-fate |
| Geode | JEE-ode | Phosphorescence | FOSS-fuh-RESS-ince |
| Glacier | GLAY-shur | Platinum | PLATT-ih-num |
| Glauberite | GLOB-ur-ite | Plutonic | plew-TONN-ick |
| Gneiss | nice | Pisolite | PIE-so-lite |
| Goethite | GET-thite | Potassium | po-TASS-ee-um |
| Granite | GRANN-it | Prehnite | PRAY-nite |
| Graphite | GRAFF-ite | Prousite | PROOS-ite |
| Gypsum | JIP-sum | Pseudowavellite | SUE-doh-WAY-vell-ite |
| Halite | HAL-ite | Psilomelane | sill-LOM-uh-lane |
| Hematite | HEM-uh-tite | Pumice | PUMM-iss |
| Heulandite | HEW-land-ite | Pyrite | PIE-rite |
| Hexagonal | hecks-AG-uh-null | Pyrolusite | PIE-ro-LEW-site |
| Hyalite | HY-uh-lite | Quartz | KWORTZ |
| Igneous | IG-nee-us | Quartzite | KWORTZ-ite |
| Illmenite | ILL-men-ite | Realgar | ree-AL-gurr |
| Isometric | eye-so-MET-trick | Resinous | REZ-uh-nuhss |
| Itacolumite | IT-uh-COLL-you-mite | Rhodocrosite | ROE-doe-KROW-site |
| Kyanite | KY-uh-nite | Rhodonite | ROE-doe-nite |
| Lapis Lazuli | LAP-iss LASS-you-lee | Rhombohedral | romm-buh-HEE-drul |
| Lava | LAH-vah | Rhyolite | RYE-o-lite |
| Lepidolite | luh-PID-uh-lite | Rosolite | ROZ-oh-lite |
| Limonite | LY-muh-nite | Rouge | roozh |
| Luminescence | lew-muh-NESS-ense | Rubellite | rew-BELL-ite |
| Magnesium | mag-NEE-shee-um | Rutile | ROO-teel |
| Malachite | MAL-uh-kite | Rutilated | ROO-till-late-ed |
| Malleable | MAL-lee-uh-bul | Sagenite | SAJ-eh-nite |
| Manganapatite | mang-gan-AP-uh-tite | Sapphire | SAFF-ire |
| Manganese | Mang-uh-NEEZ | Selenite | SELL-eh-nite |
| Marcasite | MAR-kuh-site | Serpentine | SIR-pen-tin |
| Metamorphic | met-uh-MORE-fick | Siderite | SID-ur-rite |
| Meteorite | MEE-tee-uhr-ite | Siliceous | si-LISH-us |
| Mica-schist | My-kuh-shist | Sillimanite | SILL-uh-man-nite |
| Microcline | My-kro-kline | Silicate | SIL-ih-kate |
| Mimetite | Mim-eh-tite | Smithsonite | SMITH-son-ite |
| Mispickel | Mis-PIK-el | Sodalite | So-duh-lite |
| Molybedenum | mol-LIB-duh-num | Spathic Iron | SPATH-ik |
| Muscovite | MUSS-koh-vite | Sphalerite | SFAL-uh-rite |
| Natrolite | NAT-ro-lite | Spinel | spin-NELL |
| Nepheline | NEFF-uh-lin | Spodumene | SPOD-you-meen |
| Niccolite | NICK-oh-lite | Stalactite | Stuh-LACK-tite |
| Nitrate | NIGH-trate | Stalagmite | stuh-LAG-mite |
| Novaculite | noh-VACK-you-lite | Staurolite | STAWR-uh-lite |
| Obsidian | ob-SIDD-ee-un | Steatite | STE-ah-tit |
| Ocher | O-ker | Stephanite | STEFF-uh-nite |
| Octahedron | Ock-tuh-HEE-dron | Stibnite | STIB-nite |
| Olivine | OLL-uh-veen | Stilbite | STILL-bite |
| Olivenite | OLL-uh-ve-nite | Strontianite | STRON-shi-an-ite |
| Orpiment | OR-pim-ent | Syenite | SY-eh-nite |
| Orthorhombic | or-thuh-ROMM-bick | Sylvanite | SILL-vane-ite |
| Onyx | ON-iks | Synthetic | sin-THET-ick |
| Oxide | OCK-side | Tantalite | TAN-tuh-lite |

| | | | |
|---|---|---|---|
| Tetragonal | tah-TRAG-uh-nal | Uvarovite | oo-VAR-oh-vite |
| Tetrahedrite | TET-ruh-HEE-drite | | |
| Thulite | THEW-lite | Vanadanite | van-AD-in-ite |
| Titanium | Ty-TAY-nee-um | Vanadium | van-NAY-dee-um |
| Topaz | TOE-pazz | Variscite | VAR-ih-site |
| Torbernite | TAWR-burn-ite | Verd-antique | verd-an-TEEK |
| Tourmaline | TOOR-muh-lin | Vitreous | VITT-ree-us |
| Trachyte | TRAK-ite | | |
| Travertine | TRAV-er-tin | Wavellite | WAY-vell-ite |
| Tremolite | TREM-oh-lite | Wernerite | WER-ner-ite |
| Trona | TROE-naw | Willemite | WILL-em-ite |
| Troostite | TROOS-tite | Witherite | WITH-er-ite |
| Turquoise | TURR-koyz | Wolframite | WOOL-fram-ite |
| | | Wulfenite | WOOL-fen-ite |
| Ulexite | YOU-leck-site | | |
| Unakite | YOU-naw-kite | Zeolite | ZE-oh-lite |
| Uraninite | you-RAN-ih-nite | Zincite | ZINK-ite |
| Uranophane | you-RAN-oh-fan | Zircon | ZER-con |

Copied from sheet printed by Hurlbut's Agate Shop, Rural Route No. 5, Muscatine, Iowa. Located on Highway No. 61 and 92, 4 miles south of Muscatine, Iowa. One mile north of Airport.

Contributed by Ben Baldwin

Via the Tompkins County Gem & Mineral Club bulletin "The Cayuga Gem".

# Credits

**Color Section**

C1. Smithsonian Institution
C2. Breck P. Kent
C3. Crater of Diamonds State Park
C4. Breck P. Kent
C4. (Inset) Smithsonian Institution
C5. Breck P. Kent
C6. (Top) Wards Natural Science Establishment
C6. (Bottom) Smithsonian Institution
C7. Wards Natural Science Establishment
C8. Lizzadro Museum
C9. Wards Natural Science Establishment
C10. Wards Natural Science Establishment
C11. Breck P. Kent
C12. Lizzadro Museum
C14. Wards Natural Science Establishment
C16. David Wilber
C19. Wards Natural Science Establishment
C20. Wards Natural Science Establishment
C21. Wards Natural Science Establishment
C22. Gemological Institute of America
C42. Mary A. Root
C43. Lizzadro Museum
C44. Lizzadro Museum
C45. Jim Winchell
C46. Mary A. Root
C50. Smithsonian Institution
C52. Breck P. Kent
C55. Mary A. Root
C56. Jim Winchell
C57. Breck P. Kent
C58. Mary A. Root
C59. Mary A. Root
C60. Mary A. Root
C61. Mary A. Root
C66. Mary A. Root
C67. Jim Winchell
C68. Breck P. Kent
C69. Mary A. Root
C70. Mary A. Root

C71. Breck P. Kent
C73. Mary A. Root
C74. Jim Winchell
C75. Ultraviolet Products, Inc.
C76. Ultraviolet Products, Inc.
C84. Lizzadro Museum
C85. Lizzadro Museum
C86. Lizzadro Museum
C87. Astro Minerals, Inc.
C88. American Museum of Natural History
C89. John Cubito for the American Museum of Natural History
C90. Charles Bernhard
C91. Charles Bernhard
C92. Charles Bernhard
C93. Ron Testa for Field Museum of Natural History
C94. Charles Bernhard
C95. Charles Bernhard
C97. Dr. Dearing Lewis
C98. Charles Bernhard
C99. Charles Bernhard

Frontispiece. Field Museum of Natural History
1. Field Museum of Natural History
2. Field Museum of Natural History
3. Field Museum of Natural History
6. (Left and right) Field Museum of Natural History
7. (Left) Field Museum of Natural History
8. Field Museum of Natural History
9. (Left) Field Museum of Natural History
11. The Huntington Library
12. The Huntington Library
16. Field Museum of Natural History
17. Matthew H. Nitecki for Field Museum of Natural History
18. South Dakota Department of Highways
19. Field Museum of Natural History
23. Montana Highway Commission

| | | | |
|---|---|---|---|
| 25. | Field Museum of Natural History | 73. | Field Museum of Natural History |
| 26. | William A. Garnett | 74. | Field Museum of Natural History |
| 27. | Field Museum of Natural History | 75. | Ida Mullane |
| 28. | Georgia Industry and Trade Bureau | 76. | Mary A. Root |
| 31. | (E) Field Museum of Natural History | 77. | Field Museum of Natural History |
| 31. | (F) Field Museum of Natural History | 78. | Field Museum of Natural History |
| 31. | (I) Mary A. Root | 83. | Mary A. Root |
| 47. | Mary A. Root | 84. | Field Museum of Natural History |
| 49. | Field Museum of Natural History | 90. | Field Museum of Natural History |
| 51. | General Electric Research Laboratory | 111. | Shop-Vac Corporation |
| 52. | Field Museum of Natural History | 112. | Geo-Sonics |
| 56. | Field Museum of Natural History | 121. | Charles Bernhard |
| 57. | Field Museum of Natural History | 122. | Charles Bernhard |
| 58. | Field Museum of Natural History | 123. | Charles Bernhard |
| 62. | Field Museum of Natural History | 124. | Charles Bernhard |
| 63. | Argonne National Laboratory | 125. | Charles Bernhard |
| 65. | Field Museum of Natural History | 126. | Charles Bernhard |
| 66. | Field Museum of Natural History | 127. | Charles Bernhard |
| 67. | National Aeronautics and Space Administration | 128. | Charles Bernhard |
| | | 129. | Charles Bernhard |
| 68. | Field Museum of Natural History | 130. | Charles Bernhard |
| 72. | Field Museum of Natural History | 131. | Charles Bernhard |

# Index

Numerals in italics indicate a reference to an illustration and/or the caption to an illustration.

# D

# H

# I

# Q

# R

# S

# Notes